H.M.Pettit

BANKERS, BONES & BEETLES

The Natural History Press, publisher for The American Museum of Natural History, is a division of Doubleday & Company, Inc. Directed by a joint editorial board made up of members of the staff of both the Museum and Doubleday, The Natural History Press publishes books and periodicals in all branches of the life and earth sciences, including anthropology and astronomy. The Natural History Press has its editorial offices at The American Museum of Natural History, Central Park West at 79th Street, New York, New York 10024, and its business offices at 501 Franklin Avenue, Garden City, New York.

BANKERS, BONES

&

BEETLES

The First Century of
The American Museum of
Natural History

GEOFFREY HELLMAN

PUBLISHED FOR
THE AMERICAN MUSEUM OF NATURAL HISTORY

THE NATURAL HISTORY PRESS
GARDEN CITY, NEW YORK

Much of the material in this book appeared originally in
The New Yorker, in slightly different form.

To James A. Oliver

LIST OF ILLUSTRATIONS

BANKERS, BONES & BEETLES

1

THE AMERICAN MUSEUM OF NATURAL HISTORY, the grandest and most spectacularly laid out such repository in the Western Hemisphere—more than sixteen million mammals, minerals, meteorites, jewels, insects, arachnids, birds, fish, reptiles, amphibians, fossils, artifacts, rotifers (minute aquatic animals, remarkable for the astonishing diversity of their forms), and glass models thereof—is housed in nineteen interconnected buildings on a twenty-three-acre quadrangle, once known as Manhattan Square and now officially called Roosevelt Square, that is bounded by Central Park West, Columbus Avenue, and Seventy-seventh and Eighty-first streets. Although this complex is architecturally disharmonious (from the west and the north, where its insides show, it looks like nothing on earth), three of its components have been designated by "New York Landmarks," a study published under the auspices of the Municipal Art Society of New York, as "structures of great local or regional importance which should be preserved." The first of these, begun in 1874 and completed in 1877, is the original red brick Victorian Gothic building, designed by two Englishmen who came to this country in their Victorian twenties—Calvert Vaux, one of the landscape architects of Central Park, and his colleague, Jacob Wrey Mould. The others are the façade of the south wing, constructed by J. Cleaveland Cady, the architect of the exterior of the Metropolitan Opera House, between 1890 and 1900, and cited by the Art Society as one of the finest examples of Romanesque Revival in greater New York; and, facing the Park, the Doric-colonnaded Roman Eclectic Roosevelt Memorial Building by John Russell Pope, a specialist in monumental buildings harking back to Greece and Rome, which opened for business in 1936. The Museum's thirty-eight exhibition halls, containing over two hundred habitat groups and several thousand other displays, along with the connecting Hayden Planetarium, which is administered by the Department of Astronomy, are annually visited by more than three million people. These include vast hordes of schoolchildren, whose inquisitive hands during the past three decades have worn away the bronze of three Carl Akeley lion-spearing groups in the great rotunda of the Roosevelt Memorial Building to a point where the outstretched left forepaw, nose, and tail of the central lioness and other easily accessible parts of these sculptures glisten like gold. The Museum's junior visitors, often frolicsome and sometimes out of hand, tend to clog the elevators and bug the curators, but staff criticism of them is muted, since their teacher-supervised and Museum-instructed presence (the Museum's Department of Education also teaches their *teachers*) encourages the City of New York to underwrite the institution's guard and maintenance forces to the tune of $1,850,000 a year, or approximately forty-four per cent of the total operating budget. The rest of the Museum's income derives from private endowment funds of $56,074,-391, and from membership dues, gifts, bookshop and house-magazine profits, and federal research grants, which in 1967 accounted for $850,000.

Most of the Museum's offices, study collections, and laboratories are on an enormous fifth floor that runs through the 710-foot-long Romanesque Revival units on the Seventy-seventh Street side and around the corner on Central Park West. The office rooms are high-ceilinged, mostly un-air-conditioned, and often furnished with roll-top desks. Generous bookshelves, rickety typewriters, and stuffed birds, skeletons, Peruvian artifacts, and the like abound. There is a Library of two hundred thousand books, periodicals, maps, and drawings. These offices and research facilities are staffed, consulted, and used, on the curatorial and research-associate level, by some hundred and twenty-five men and women, nearly all of them doctors of philosophy, science, literature, or law. In private life, the Museum's advanced (or honorary) academicians are often greeted as Mister (or Mrs. or Miss), but on the premises they are almost invariably hailed as Doctor. An exception exists in the person of M. Jean Delacour, a renowned French naturalist who has been a Research Associate in Ornithology since 1944 and who spends several months a year in this country writing books about birds at his Museum desk. (Research Associates, who are given houseroom but no salaries, are, typically, scientifically in-

clined men and women of means, former curators, and
investigators from other institutions.) Delacour, whose
Château de Clères in Normandy boasts a park stocked
with avicultural and other collections of living animals
obtained from his own expeditions and from collectors
on his payroll, possesses an honorary doctorate from the
University of Lille, but he likes to be called Captain, a
title dating from his service in the French Army in the
First World War. The Museum indulges Captain Delacour,
who has given it a great many non-living birds, but it
prefers to call its friends Doctor whenever this is feasible
and sometimes when it isn't. Its *Annual Report* is one
of the few publications in which the author of *The Lone
Star Ranger, The Wanderer of the Wasteland,* and *The
Call of the Canyon* is called Dr. Zane Grey, and in
which the president of the Chase Manhattan Bank is called
Dr. David Rockefeller. Dr. Grey, a Doctor of Dental
Surgery at the University of Pennsylvania, gave the Museum some of its largest salt-water fishes in 1926, including
a sunfish that weighed a ton. Dr. Rockefeller, an amateur
coleopterist, has presented it with thousands of beetles
and the land for the Southwestern Research Station in
Portal, Arizona, one of four Museum-owned or Museum-
connected field stations. (The others are the Archbold
Biological Station in Lake Placid, Florida; the Kalbfleisch
Field Research Station in Huntington, Long Island; and
the Lerner Marine Laboratory in Bimini, Bahamas.)

Dr. Rockefeller is a perfectly good University of Chicago Ph.D., but his academic title is a contagious appella-
tion on the Museum's terrain. Visiting researchers, less
grandly accredited, have occasionally been startled, after

becoming familiar figures in the Museum Library or in the study-collection rooms, by being addressed as Doctor by the staff. Curatorial non-doctors were tolerated—nay, welcomed—in the Museum's early days, but today no top departmental post is open to an unadorned Mister. Until quite recently, a great and exceptional throwback to a more permissive period survived in the shape of Mr. Charles M. (Chuck) Bogert, who became an Assistant Curator of Herpetology in 1940, full curator in 1943, and was chairman of the department from 1944 to 1968. For twenty-one years, Mr. Bogert, whose professional standing is such that he has served as president of the American Society of Ichthyologists and Herpetologists, was the only full curator whom the *Annual Report* had to call Mister. Bogert is a philosophical man, preoccupied with snakes, frogs, and toads (he maintains a small zoo of living snakes in his office suite), and this may or may not have nettled him, but it *did* nettle Mrs. Bogert. At a Museum cocktail party celebrating the opening of the Hall of Indians of the Eastern Woodlands in the spring of 1966, she was overheard to say, "We're going out to the University of California next week. Thank goodness, I think Chuck's going to get it." The University, her husband's alma mater, came through with an LL.D.

Many of the Museum's doctors spend part of their time helping to turn out other doctors. A number of them double as Columbia, New York University, and City University professors, conducting undergraduate and postgraduate courses that give credit to candidates for degrees, including doctorates. Along with such tasks, and between intermittent periods of concentrated work called for by the installation of new halls (thirteen completed since the beginning of an expanded exhibition program in 1959), nearly all of the Museum's doctors are busy, generally in the summer but sometimes for several years on end, with outdoor research on things like (to quote from a recent list of projects) "The Differentiation of the Dwarf Toads of the *Bufo fergusoni* Group in Peninsular India and Ceylon" (Dr. Bogert), "A New Wolf Spider from the Southeastern United States" (Dr. Willis J. Gertsch, an Entomology curator in charge of spiders), "Systematic and Zoogeographic Survey of Killifishes of the Western North Atlantic" (Dr. Donn E. Rosen, chairman of Ichthyology), "Survey of the Fossil and Recent Molluscan Faunas of the Galápagos Islands" (Dr. William K. Emerson, chairman of Living Invertebrates), and "Population Dynamics of Ant-Following Antbirds on Barro Colorado Island, Panama Canal Zone" (Dr. Edwin O. Willis, Ornithology Research Fellow). The doctors also go in for indoor research on such subjects as "Accumulation of Data Relating to the Scroll-Wing Motif in Early China and Mesoamerica" (Dr. Gordon F. Ekholm, Curator of Mexican Archeology in the Department of Anthropology), "Revision of North American Mid-Tertiary Camels" (Dr. Malcolm C. McKenna, Associate Curator of the Frick Collection in the Department of Vertebrate Paleontology), and "Changes in Mating Behavior in Adult Female Cats Following Desensitization of the Genitalia." Dr. Lester R. Aronson, the Museum's cat-mating man, whose previous findings revealed that among *male* cats "after desensitization of a specific penial nerve, positional disorientation in relation to the female occurs during sexual contact," is head of the Department of Animal Behavior, a predominatingly research arm of the Museum that keeps a collection of living, breathing cats, rats, fish, ants, and birds in an attic and a glass-housed aquarium on the top of the original building, where it studies their behavior. Besides fooling around with the sex life of scientifically disturbed cats, it measures the vision of starlings; cases the adjustment of kittens, under varying induced conditions, to their mothers and other members of the litter; and examines the effects of stress (again, scientifically induced) on rats. The Museum's investigations have given rise to the publication of innumerable house treatises and monographs (issued in a series of fat books called *Bulletins* and brief papers called *Novitates,* meaning "new acquaintances"), along with extra-house books, on everything from the cranial variation found in a single population of Uruguayan hog-nosed skunks and the presence of chitin in certain groups of invertebrates to an interpretation of ritualistic combat between conspecific male snakes (meaning snakes of the same species) and the evolution of sharks. Freedom to carry on this sort of research has caused Dr. Harry L. Shapiro, chairman of the Department of Anthropology and the senior curator in point of tenure (and the author, *inter alia,* of genetic studies of the Pitcairn Islanders and Chinese and Japanese population elements in Hawaii), to say, "I feel a great devotion to the Museum. You write your own ticket as a scientist—this has been my experience, anyway." And the research itself, along with the Museum's teaching activities, has enabled the Encyclopaedia Britannica to describe the institutional source of this knowledge and dissemination, without fear of successful contradiction, as "a center for the study of many scientific problems of world concern."

A number of the scientific articles in the Encyclopaedia (although not the one from which the above quotation is taken) have been written by Museum staff members, past and present. The lion's share of "Rotifera," for example, is the product of Dr. Libbie H. Hyman, a Department of Living Invertebrates Research Associate and a fellow-Ph.D. of Dr. Rockefeller at the University of Chicago, now in her eighties, part of whose income comes from books about minute aquatic animals bearing titles like *Protozoa Through Ctenophora; Platyhelminthes and Rynchocoela; Acanthocephala, Aschelminthes, and Endoprocta;* and *Smaller Coelomate Groups: Chaetognatha, Hemichordata, Pogonophora, Phoronida, Ectoprata, Brachiopoda, Sipunculida, and Coelomate Bilateria,* illustrated with scientific line drawings by the author. Dr. Hyman, who lives around the corner from the Museum and lunches in her office on bread, cheese, and vegetable juice, was in vertebrates before she saw the light and got into the aforementioned *in*vertebrate worms, fishes, and mollusks. "Oh, the time I wasted on vertebrates!" she said to a reporter a few years ago, when she was awarded the Gold Medal of the Linnean Society of London for zoology. "My original manual on them was published in 1922, and in the 1940s I spent three years on a revised edition. The two editions have sold over two hundred thousand copies, and I don't know what to do with the money, but I still don't like vertebrates. I don't know *why* I don't like them."

Dr. Hyman's museum (and picnic ground) is referred

to by most New Yorkers without its initial adjective, but in its habitat it is always called The American Museum—except, perhaps, by its telephone-switchboard girls, who, when people call up, simply say, "Museum." The Museum is jealous of its name. In 1914, when a Department of Parks sign near it in Central Park read, "To the Museum of Natural History," one of its trustees, Mr. Madison Grant, wrote the Museum's president, Dr. Henry Fairfield Osborn, "I think the Museum would do well to replace this at its own expense with a statement, 'To The American Museum of Natural History.'" Dr. Osborn took the matter up with the Commissioner of Parks, and the change was made.

The American Museum owes its existence primarily to Mr. Albert S. Bickmore, a man whose approach to the products of nature and the culture of man was initially, and indeed remained, more exuberant than scientific. The Museum's "revered founder," as he was called on his death in 1914 by President Osborn—or, as Bickmore was later acclaimed by the Dictionary of American Biography (DAB), the "Father of the Museum"—was born in 1839 in Tenants Harbor, midway on the coast of Maine, in the commodious Mansion House, as it was locally known, of his father, a sea captain and shipbuilder. "When I was eight years old," the son recalled in 1908, in an unpublished autobiography, "my father, who was Captain of a fine barque, took my mother, my sister, and myself to Bordeaux, France. Our cargo on the outward voyage was staves, and we brought back wines, particularly the claret for which that part of France is famous." He went on, after this lapse of sixty-one years, to celebrate the grapevines of the Médoc, but he was formed by the natural wonders of Maine. "Our house was connected by a long shed to a large barn, which had on its side toward the sun and the seashore . . . rows of several hundred nests of the barn swallow, and large flocks of these half-tame birds were constantly circling round our home from early spring time till late in the autumn," he wrote, and continued:

The neighboring sea abounded with marine life. Great schools of herring, alewives, menhaden, mackerel and pollock came up in the spring and early summer from out of the deep ocean and swarmed among the islands and into every inlet and harbor along the shore. Pursuing and preying on them came immense numbers of food fishes like the cod, the hake, and the haddock. Seals feasted on these fishes and at low water almost covered the ledges where they were basking in the sunshine. . . .

The harbors then swarmed with such numbers of great lobsters that while a boy I have many times gathered a bushel of them from their hiding places under rocks and old wrecks in a single low tide. Such splendid specimens could not now be found by searching for them during half a summer.

Our house was located between a forest and the sea. The spruce and fir trees behind it were loaded with cones which furnished an ample supply of food to a colony of red squirrels, and wild rabbits scampered away before us as we followed the narrow and shaded paths through the woods. . . . In spring time with two companions of my own age, we learned where to find the large blue violets and where the small, white, sweet-scented ones abounded on the banks of running brooks. . . . We knew well where the robins and sparrows and many other birds built their nests and reared their young, and we could recognize most of them by their calls and always, toward sunset, listened for the rich liquid notes of the thrushes.

The annual migration of the sea birds was a subject of
the greatest interest—especially that of the Wild Goose, which
always flew in triangular lines, and gave a peculiar "honk"
announcing far in advance that they were coming. . . .
Every landscape view from our old homestead contained
the conspicuous nest of a pair of fishhawks, usually perched on
the upper limbs of the highest tree in all the neighborhood.
. . . As the bays and inlets abounded with fishes, it was a
constant delight to watch these birds sailing to and fro until
some scaly inhabitant of the deep happened to come near the
surface of the water, when the nearest fishhawk would poise
itself for a moment, with its wings raised up high above its
head, and then plunge down with almost unfailing aim upon
its finny prey. . . . The special occasion of the year was
when several families of the Penobscot Indians came back to
their annual camping place on one of our beaches. . . . The
crude appearance of their primitive shelters was in marked
contrast with the beautiful baskets of manifold colors which
were made by the squaws.

This fortunate youth graduated in 1860 from Dart-
mouth, where he specialized in chemistry, geology, and
mineralogy. He moved on to Cambridge, Mass., to study
natural history under Louis Agassiz, the famous Swiss-
born naturalist who had just founded the Museum of
Comparative Zoology at Harvard and was running it with
an irascible hand. Agassiz, thirty-seven years Bickmore's
senior, soon made his pupil one of his assistants. "My
enjoyable labor in his institution was to help take care
of the Radiates and Mollusks," Bickmore has written,
and, again, "One of the greatest privileges of studying
with Agassiz was to live in the delightful atmosphere of
enthusiasm which always made his presence inspiring."
Nowhere in his memoirs is there any overt criticism of his
peppery chief, but the following passage gives a clue to

an early rift in the lute, and more than a clue to the genesis
of the New York museum:

Harvard University has always had a magnetic attraction for
visitors from London. . . . The most distinguished of such
guests formed the royal party of the Prince of Wales, now
Edward VII, who visited America under the direction of
the Duke of Newcastle in 1861.

One of the days of his visit to Boston was devoted to
Cambridge. When they came to our museum Agassiz met
them at the entrance and taking the arm of the Prince led
the way through our halls. Next in order came the Duke
and with him a tall gentleman having a peculiarly graceful
manner and refined air. He proved to be the famous Doctor
[Sir Henry Wentworth] Acland of Oxford University, the
man selected by the late Queen . . . to be the tutor and
personal advisor of the future King. Our Professor's plan
for receiving companies of visitors was to place each of his
students in the room where were displayed the specimens
under his care, and in this way each of us was afforded an
opportunity of meeting our distinguished guests . . .

After the royal party had left the building, I remained
alone in the unbroken silence to gain an hour's more study
in the fading twilight, when, looking down Divinity Avenue,
arched over by its magnificent elms, I saw this same remarkable man approaching unattended. I knew he was coming to
the museum, for Agassiz had often told us of Doctor Acland
and of the great museum of natural history he had just
created in Oxford. He wished to go through our institution
again and take time to note its treasures. He enquired for
the Professor, and I replied that he had gone to his home,
but that I would be more than gratified to conduct him
through our halls and answer any questions within my limited
knowledge.

As we were walking quietly along together, after some
preliminary conversation, I ventured to say to him, "Doctor
Acland, may I be permitted to ask you a question?" He
promptly and cordially replied, "Certainly, my young friend.

What is your question?" "Does it seem strange to you, sir, that Agassiz, our great teacher, should have located his museum of natural history for future America out here in Cambridge, while in Europe the institutions of this character are placed in the political and monetary capitals of the several empires, as London, Paris, Berlin, Vienna, and elsewhere, except your own museum in Oxford, which Agassiz always describes to us as the model one of them all?" "Yes," he answered, "it does seem strange, but what has suggested such a question to your mind?" I said, "Nearly all of the prominent men who visit our country come here to Cambridge and call on Professor Agassiz, and I have noticed that several of these gentlemen of broad and unbiased views have given partial expression to such a suggestion, for they have seemed to think that to reach our museum they had travelled nearly as far from New York, where the most of them had landed, as they had to come over the sea at all (sic)." I also remarked, in substance, that as science does not appear to create wealth directly, but only to use it for the higher and nobler purpose of promoting original research, it seemed to me natural that an institution, which must depend upon the interest which rich and generous men may take in it for its existence and prosperity, should be located in the immediate vicinity of their homes. Now New York (I said) is our city of the greatest wealth and therefore probably the best location for the future museum of natural history for our whole land.

In reply to this lengthy explanation of my views, he simply turned toward me, and, looking me straight in the eye, said, "My young friend, that is a grand thought."

This hearty endorsement by such an eminent authority of the desirability and feasibility of my youthful vision so completely captivated my imagination that I at once determined that I would work for nothing else by day and dream of nothing else by night until I had, at least in some degree, aided in establishing a museum of natural history upon Manhattan Island.

A more forthright picture of the Agassiz-Bickmore relationship is provided by Professor Edward Lurie, of

Wayne State University, in *Louis Agassiz: A Life in Science,* which states:

> Agassiz felt that his students were not yet ready to publish
> their research and refused to grant them permission to do
> so. . . . Argument ensued, with Agassiz particularly furious
> over the fact that . . . Bickmore and others had tried to
> arrange for positions in Salem, Massachusetts, and New York
> City without his knowledge. Bickmore went so far as to
> solicit a popular subscription for a private research project
> of his own. . . . By December, 1863 . . . Agassiz had had
> enough of such behavior and . . . refused to recommend to
> the faculty the permanent appointment of his students as
> museum assistants. Thus . . . Bickmore (and others) all left
> the museum. . . . Bickmore decided to found a museum of
> his own, which would be run on "democratic principles" in
> distinction to the "dictatorial methods" employed at Cam-
> bridge. . . . Bickmore's defiant declaration proved to be no
> idle boast, for he was able to interest a group of prominent
> New Yorkers in his idea and thereby provided the stimulus
> for what eventually became the American Museum of Natural
> History.

Bickmore's private research project was a sixteen-month, 6,000-mile trip through the Malay Archipelago and the Dutch East Indies, undertaken for the stated purpose "of collecting the beautiful shells of those seas." He followed this up with a year and a half in China, Japan, Siberia, and Europe. "I carried with me everywhere two things, a Bible and a sketch of a plan for a museum in New York," he wrote in his unpublished memoir. Back in Boston at the end of 1867, he lectured at this city's Society of Natural History on "The Ainos, or Hairy Men of Yesso" and "The Ainos, or Hairy Men of Saghalien and

the Kurile Islands." A reasonably hairy man himself, with
a flowing beard, he is depicted, in full whisker, under
the caption "Saved by Grasping a Fern," in the frontispiece of *Travels in the East Indian Archipelago*, a book
he wrote on his return, and, again, in the last of this
volume's thirty-six illustrations, under the title, "Killing
the Python." Although he lived another forty-five years
or so, *Travels*, which was dedicated "to the generous
friends of science . . . through whose liberality the travels herein described were made," was the only book Mr.
Bickmore ever published. Some of its descriptions make
it seem a pity that their author never got between covers
again. "Our bill of fare was sufficient to satisfy the most
fastidious epicure," he wrote, for example, of a Javanese
dinner party, and went on:

> . . . All was prepared in an unexceptional manner, and the
> rich display of pineapples, mangostins, dukus, and several
> kinds of bananas was finer than many a European prince
> could set before his guests. The process of demolishing had
> full begun, when the dark beauties, who had been dancing
> before the house, came in, and ranged themselves round the
> table. My first impression was that they had come in to see
> how Europeans eat, and I only refrained from hinting to that
> effect to the Resident on my right, because he had already
> smiled to see my surprise at our novel reception, and besides,
> I was anxious not to appear to be wholly ignorant of their
> odd customs. Soon they began to sing, and this, I thought
> to myself, is probably what is meant by a sumptuous banquet
> in the East. . . . As the song continued, one after another
> took out a handkerchief of spotless white, and, folding it
> into a triangular form, began to fan the gentleman in front
> of her. This is indeed Eastern luxury, I said to myself, and
> while I was wondering what would come next, the damsel

behind the Resident reached forward and gave him a loud kiss on his cheek. "That was intended as an appetizer I presume?" *Natuurlijk,* "Of course," he replied, and I leaned back in my chair to give way to a hearty laugh, which I had been trying for a long time to restrain, when suddenly I was astonished by a similar salutation on the lips! It was done so quickly that I had no time to recover from my bewildering surprise, and cooly explain that such was not the custom in my land. Instead of my laughing at the Resident's expense, the whole party laughed at mine; but my confusion was dispelled by the assurance of all that even the governor-general himself had to submit to such treatment when he came to inspect these islands. Besides, I was made aware that the fault was largely my own, and that, when I leaned backward to laugh, the fair one behind me had misinterpreted the movement as a challenge (which she certainly seemed not loath to accept). At every village we had to run a similar gantlet, and I must confess that several times it occurred to me that the youngest member of the party certainly received his share of such tender attention, and that many of these beauties, *nona itum,* were determined to improve their present opportunity for fear that they might never again have the privilege of kissing a gentleman with a white face.

His literary work out of the way, the well-bussed duku fancier, whom a contemporary has described as a "live wire," began to buttonhole his group of prominent New Yorkers. He was, at the time, stationed at Madison (now Colgate) University, in Hamilton, New York, as professor of zoology and geology, but his campus duties seem to have allowed time for expeditions to Manhattan business circles. William E. Dodge, Jr., a Phelps-Dodge copper scion, shell collector, and friend of science and other good works who had helped underwrite the Bickmore trip, now revisited by the Professor (the title by which

Bickmore was universally hailed), said that he was too busy putting up a building for the Y.M.C.A. to do much about a natural-history museum himself, but he gave Bickmore a letter of introduction to a fellow philanthropist—Theodore Roosevelt, the father of T.R. (then ten years old), who had inherited a plate-glass business on Maiden Lane and was active in the Children's Aid Society. Other Bickmore contacts among rich and generous men were Benjamin H. Field, a retired merchant of whom the Encyclopaedia of Contemporary Biography of New York was to write in 1882, "Scarcely a reputable charity in New York is a stranger to his benefactions"; Robert Colgate, a soap manufacturer; William A. Haines, a wholesale dry goods merchant; D. Jackson Steward, an amateur conchologist; and Robert L. Stuart, a sugar refiner who was an original backer of the A.S.P.C.A. and Presbyterian Hospital. Although several of these men, like Mr. Dodge and Mr. Steward, had cabinets of shells, they were not particularly interested in the spectrum of natural history. They were, however, patriotic New Yorkers, painfully aware that their city, with nothing of any public consequence in this line, was outdistanced not only by Cambridge and Boston, whose Society of Natural History dated from 1830, but by Philadelphia, where an Academy of Natural Sciences had been organized in 1812, and by the nation's capital, where Spencer F. Baird, the ornithologist, was whipping the Smithsonian's natural history museum into shape. Their motivation, and that of others who joined them in supporting the Museum after it got going, is well set forth in the minutes of an 1890 trustees' meeting

marking the death of Mr. Hugh Auchincloss, a member
of the board:

> In associating himself with us, Mr. Auchincloss was not
> prompted by any peculiar interest in any special branch of
> science, but by the larger view of affording support and
> encouragement to an enterprise embracing a wide field, de-
> signed to aid in freeing his native city from something like
> scientific aridity, and to establish a center of scientific interest
> and entertainment in the midst of the manifold life of a
> great metropolis.

Roosevelt and the rest were eager to dissipate this arid-
ity. Meetings, sparkplugged by the Professor, were held at
some of their homes, and in December, 1868, nineteen of
the conferees addressed a letter to the Commissioners of
Central Park, which read:

> A number of gentlemen have long desired that a great Mu-
> seum of Natural History should be established in Central
> Park, and having now the opportunity of securing a rare
> and very valuable collection as a nucleus of such Museum,
> the undersigned wish to enquire if you are disposed to provide
> for its reception and development.

The undersigned of this historic feeler, besides the afore-
mentioned, consisted of James Brown and Howard Potter,
partners in the then commanding banking house of Brown
Brothers; Levi P. Morton and George Bliss of Morton,
Bliss & Co.; three other influential bankers, Adrian Iselin,
Morris K. Jesup, and J. P. Morgan; William T. Blodgett,
a real-estate owner and varnish manufacturer; Marshall O.
Roberts, a Civil War steamship millionaire; Alexander T.
Stewart, proprietor of the largest retail store in the world;

John D. Wolfe, a retired merchant; and two copper mag-
nates, Isaac N. Phelps and A. G. Phelps Dodge, a brother
of William. Their prayer was granted—"The Commissioners . . . will very gladly receive the collection . . . and
will use their best exertions toward the establishment of a
Museum of Natural History," Andrew H. Green, Comp-
troller of Central Park, replied—and on January 19, 1869,
most of the signers, plus four new sponsors, met in Mr.
Field's house and appointed a committee to raise funds to
purchase the rare and valuable collection. This consisted
of several thousand mounted birds, mounted animals, and
mounted skeletons of mammals, birds, reptiles, and fishes
assembled by Edouard Verreaux, a Paris naturalist, who
had recently died. The museum's sponsors decided, additionally, to seek a charter for their institution, and placed
this matter in the hands of Mr. Joseph H. Choate, the lawyer, whom Bickmore, via a letter of introduction from
Roosevelt, had recruited to the cause. Choate drew up a
document calling for a Museum and Library of Natural
History "for the purpose . . . of encouraging and develop-
ing the study of Natural Science [and] of advancing the
general knowledge of kindred subjects, and to that end of
furnishing popular instruction and recreation." It devolved
upon Bickmore to take the next step. A great chap for getting letters of introduction, he obtained one from Samuel J.
Tilden, a political Pooh Bah who later became governor
of New York, to State Senator William M. Tweed, a man
not generally known for his good works. Bickmore presented this to Tweed in his Albany hotel, where a rather
curious interview took place.

I found him to be a man of portly dimensions and comfortably seated in a large arm chair [Bickmore writes]. I introduced myself and my business by saying, "Senator, I am honored by your friend Mr. Samuel J. Tilden, with this letter, and I have also these other letters from other leading citizens in New York City." "Well, well, what can I do for Mr. Tilden?" "These gentlemen, Senator, whose names are on this paper [the would-be incorporators—Roosevelt, Wolfe, Stuart, Jesup, Iselin, Blodgett, Morgan, *et al*], have asked me to state to you that they desire to found a Museum of Natural History in New York, and if possible on Central Park, similar to Professor Agassiz's great museum in Cambridge—you know of that institution, Senator?" "Certainly! Certainly!" was his prompt reply (and now I must confess that for an instant a cruel doubt flashed over my mind as to whether he had ever really heard its name mentioned before in all his life). . . . I continued, "Senator, I hope you will agree with these gentlemen that to found such a grand institution as they have in mind it is proper and necessary for them to have a charter, creating them a body corporate by a special act of the Legislature, and Mr. Joseph H. Choate, whom you know well?"—"Yes, he is a partner of Mr. Evarts"—"has carefully prepared this draft of a bill . . . and they have requested me to respectfully solicit you to do them the important favor to take charge of this measure." "All right, my young friend, I will see your bill safely through," was his reply as he thrust our carefully prepared document into his capacious outside pocket. . . .

Tweed was as good as his word: on April 9, 1869, the necessary act was signed by Governor John T. Hoffman, a creature of Tweed's. "It certainly proved to be wise that we asked Senator Tweed to take charge of this important measure," Bickmore has written, "because with his endorsement its prompt passage was assured, and also because it was certain that it would not be amended in the slightest degree, for no legislator . . . dared to suggest

the slightest modification to a bill which had been introduced by Mr. Tweed." It is a melancholy commentary on
political life that both Choate and Tilden were instrumen-
tal in sending Tweed—who was, in a way, too, the Father
of the Museum—to prison four years later.

The Museum's first board of trustees, which included
most of the Central Park petitioners, elected as its president Mr. Wolfe, then seventy-seven. Next, raising its sights
from the limitations of the Verreaux-collection committee, which had scarcely got under way, it launched a
fund drive for natural science specimens in general. Bickmore, working under Roosevelt's direction out of a room
loaned to him by Brown Brothers, was the prime mover
in this, operating on a commission basis. "As he unrolled
the document," he wrote of the plate-glass manufacturer's
reception of an early progress report, "there came over
his face first an expression of surprise and then of radiant
delight." By the end of the year, fifty-two thousand
dollars had been obtained from some sixty sources bearing
names like Brown; Wolfe; Stewart; Stuart; Steward; Jesup;
Colgate; Morgan; Field; Iselin; Roosevelt; Morton, Bliss
& Co.; Arnold Constable & Co.; Samuel F. B. Morse;
and Peter Cooper. Of this, $44,500 had been raised by
Bickmore, who received four hundred and forty-five dollars in commissions.

The money was put to use as soon as it began coming in.
As things turned out, the Verreaux specimens (the Museum opted for thirty-four hundred of these, mostly birds),
which cost sixteen thousand dollars, were outnucleused,
by a few weeks, by twenty-five hundred North American
birds purchased for seventy-three hundred dollars from

Daniel G. Elliot, and by the acquisition, negotiated by
Messrs. Blodgett and Elliot on a European trip, of four
thousand mounted birds, six hundred mounted mammals,
and two thousand fishes and reptiles, mounted or pickled,
from the heir of Prince Maximilian of Neuwied, a German
explorer of Brazil. The sum of fifteen hundred pounds was
sent to Brown, Shipley & Co., the Museum's London
bankers, to buy these, of which Mr. Blodgett wrote in
the Museum's first *Annual Report:* "We were informed by
competent experts that the cost of mounting this collection
exceeds the price we paid for it." Presents also began to
arrive. In 1869, Mr. Coleman T. Robinson gave ten thousand butterflies and moths, covering three thousand species; and another entomologically inclined donor, Baron
R. Osten-Sacken, the Russian consul-general in New York,
sent along thirty-eight hundred insects, mostly beetles.
The Museum had no home, and its birds, bugs, and so
forth were at first stored, exotically, at Brown Brothers.
Early in 1870, the trustees persuaded the Central Park
Commissioners to give them exhibition space in the two
upper stories of the Arsenal Building, on the east side of
the Park at Sixty-fourth Street, and to provide them with
suitable cases. Professor Bickmore, who had resigned from
Madison University to become the Museum's superintendent, "to take charge of collections," began to get things
in shape. In 1871, he engaged as his assistant Dr. Joseph
B. Holder, who, as surgeon-in-chief to the government
engineers on the Florida reef, had made a zoological and
botanical survey of this topographical feature for Agassiz
and Baird. Bickmore and Holder, joined by the latter's
nineteen-year-old son, Charles, classified and arranged the

collections, which were opened to the public that spring. President Wolfe died a year later; he had lived just long enough to see the dawn of success. His successor, Mr. Stuart, reviewing the seminal Arsenal days in the 1872 *Annual Report*, observed that "on nearly every day during fair weather, our halls have been thronged by visitors, not only from our own city and state, but from all parts of the country, numbering frequently from 5000 to 10,-000." The halls, by this time, had been additionally enriched by scores of donations, among them a fur seal, a giraffe, and a baboon from Mr. P. T. Barnum; a number of carcasses from the adjacent Central Park Menagerie (with which the Museum had, and still has, a mortuary-gift agreement); two hornets' nests from Mr. H. W. Mc-Koon, of Sullivan County, New York, who wrote: "Believing a National Museum of Nautcheral (sic) History is a National Blessing I am ready and anxious to aid the enterprise in every way that I can"; and "1 Bat, 12 Mice, 1 Turtle, 1 Skull, Red Squirrel; and 4 Birds Eggs" from Mr. Theodore Roosevelt, Jr., whose father had brought him in while Bickmore and the Holders were unpacking the Verreaux specimens.

The Arsenal space, at once filled to capacity, had been obtained as a temporary, emergency stopgap; in 1871, the Museum had joined the Metropolitan Museum of Art (incorporated a year after it) in a successful petition to the state legislature for permanent sites and suitable fire-proof buildings. On June 2, 1874, the cornerstone of the American Museum was laid by President Grant with a trowel bought from Tiffany's. "My dear Mr. Haines," the founding Roosevelt had written his fellow vice-president on the board of trustees a few days before, "By all means order the trowel, one must certainly have it and the President is entitled to a good one." Grant's chore was preceded by speeches by President Stuart (who characterized New York's answer to Boston and Philadelphia as "a grand collection of specimens," "a source of public amusement," and "a means of general instruction"); the president of the Department of Parks ("What nobler exhibitions could be given of the crowning achievements of this municipality than those which the Museum and its sister institution, the Art Gallery [i.e., the Met], will afford? This peerless pleasure ground for the people, which will proudly boast of these twin jewels as its legitimate offspring, will contain within itself in miniature the records of the progress of the country"); Governor John A. Dix of New York ("It is pleasant to see a great metropolitan city like this, casting aside for the moment the habiliments of its industry, to lay the foundation of a Museum in which the dead past is to be linked to the living present"); and Professor Joseph Henry, who, as secretary of the Smithsonian Institution, had recently sent the Museum "several specimens of mummies from a cave in the Aleutian Islands" and who now, seizing upon the occasion to vent his pet peeve, the architectural extravagance of *his* institution's building, said, in part:

> [The American Museum] is to be a temple of nature in which the productions of the inorganic and organic world, together with the remnants of the past ages of the human family are to be collected, classified, and properly exhibited. It is to be rendered an attractive exhibition which shall arrest the attention of the most unobserving of those who, having

been confined all their lives to the city, have come to consider
edifices of brick and of stone as the most prominent objects
of the physical world. . . . It is a melancholy fact that,
notwithstanding the reputation for wealth and intelligence
possessed by our people, for the only institution intended
especially for the advancement of science in this country we
are indebted to a foreigner, James Smithson, and that a very
large portion of the income of this had wrongfully been
devoted to the erection of a costly edifice and the embellish-
ment of grounds.

President Grant's trowel was swiped by someone who
felt that *he* was entitled to a good one ("After the laying
of the cornerstone," the man who brought it over from
Tiffany's later reported, "General Grant left the trowel
on the cornerstone, and when it occurred to Professor
Bickmore to look for it, it had disappeared, probably
forever"), and the cornerstone itself, containing a copper
box stuffed with Museum and Parks Department reports,
a manual of the state legislature, a Congressional Direc-
tory, copies of twelve New York newspapers, three magazines, a paper dollar, a silver dollar, and some small change,
also disappeared, or was lost, probably forever. No one at
the Museum today knows where it is, and no one knew
on September 17, 1941, when Mr. Wayne M. Faunce, vice-
director and executive secretary of the temple of nature,
wrote the late Edward Ringwood Hewitt, the country's
leading dry-fly trout fisherman:

I recall that at one of the annual meetings of the Anglers
Club, held in the American Museum of Natural History, you
referred to the fact that you had been present at the laying
of the cornerstone of the Museum. It is a source of chagrin

that no one now connected with the Museum knows the
location of this cornerstone. . . . Can you throw any light
on the matter?

Mr. Hewitt was seven years old when the cornerstone
was laid. He was a son of Abram S. Hewitt, an early
trustee, and a grandson of Peter Cooper, the founder of
Cooper Union, who, besides money, gave the Museum its
first whale skeleton. This had originally been earmarked
for a museum of curiosities in the Union, which opened
in 1859, but was released, and badly in need of an institutional home, when this projected feature was bumped
by a reading room. E. R. Hewitt may have been taken
to the Museum's 1874 ceremonies by his father or grandfather, or both. His spelling and punctuation, to the end
of his days remained idiosyncratic; for one thing, he was
a foe of the comma. He answered the vice-director on
his typewriter:

My dear Mr. Faunce.
I was only a small boy when the corner stone of the
Museum was laid and the wholeplace was covered with a
cloth except the stone. There would be no way in which
a small boy could tell where it was as there was a wooden
stand erectd all over the place. I cant see that the location
of the corner stone is a matter of any importance at all.
Yours truly.

There the matter rests; the Museum is in good company, since no one at the Smithsonian knows where *its*
cornerstone, laid in 1847, is, either.

The new building—the Vaux-Mould Victorian Gothic
one—was designed, as the first of a series that would

eventually occupy the entire square, after rough interior plans drawn up by Professor Bickmore. Well supplied with glass for its windows and showcases by Mr. Roosevelt's firm, it opened on December 22, 1877. President Rutherford B. Hayes was on hand; laudatory speeches abounded. "Its durability, abundance, and perfect diffusion of light are evident to all," President Stuart said, and he also touched on New York's regional cultural inferiority complex:

> For many years, those of our people who were privileged to travel abroad were constantly reminded of the fact that in our own wealthy and influential metropolis there were no such institutions for the higher cultivation of the people and their instruction and recreation as the Museums existing not only in the capitals of Europe, but even in places of moderate population. Many of the students of natural science, who grew up in our midst, moved away to the neighboring cities, which possessed such attractions, and New York came to be regarded as so given over to the accumulation of wealth as to be too sterile a soil for the cultivation of the higher branches of education.

"In whose honor are the chief personages of the nation, state, and city here assembled? Whose palace is this? What divinity is worshipped in this place?" Dr. Charles W. Eliot, the president of Harvard, started out, and went on, without mentioning Darwin's name, to hail "the stupendous doctrine of hereditary transmission," which he felt, hopefully, would "enhance the natural interest in vigorous family stocks . . . give a rational basis for penal legislation, and promote both the occasional production of illustrious men and the gradual improvement of the masses of mankind." Professor Othniel C. Marsh, director of the Pea-

body Museum of Natural History at Yale, stressed research. "These vast collections will spread the elements
of Natural Science among the people of New York and
the surrounding region, but the quiet workers in the attic,
who pursue Science for its own sake, will bring the Museum renown throughout the world."

Professor Marsh was right in the long run, but the fact
is that no sooner had the Museum jumped across the Park
than it almost went out of business. The peerless pleasure
ground of the people had only recently been cleaned out
of a litter of squatters, shanties, goats, and kitchen gardens.
"It was practically out in the country then," the *Sun*
wrote of Manhattan Square in 1911, referring to the time
of the 1871 Act. "If the superintendent had wanted to
secure a collection of goats or mongrel dogs or stray cats
he could have found them right on the site of the building
that was to be. When the cornerstone of the first section
of that building was laid . . . the goats looked on at
quite an imposing ceremony." The superintendent himself
has written, "The next day after our grandly successful
opening we experienced the depressing effect of finding
our spacious exhibition halls nearly deserted. We were . . .
doomed . . . for a number of years to experience the
unfavorable effect of our isolated position as compared to
our former location in the old Arsenal, near the main
entrance to Central Park." Indeed, in 1880, when, for
lack of space in its already crowded palace, the Museum
was still housing the McKoon hornets' nests and a good
many of the Verreaux mammals, Maximilian fishes, and
Osten-Sacken insects in the Arsenal, Jesup wrote Stuart,
"On my visit to the Arsenal there were at least twice as

many visitors looking at remnants of the old collections as there were in the main building on my visit there." The vast collections, around the time of Mr. Jesup's visits, had been swollen by gifts from many illustrious men —among them, Samuel Sloan, president of the Delaware, Lackawanna and Western Railroad ("thirteen boxes specimens Copper and Iron Ores, from Lake Superior District"); Henry G. Marquand, a founder of the Metropolitan Museum who became president of it and of the St. Louis, Iron Mountain and Southern Railroad Company ("five barrels of pottery from the Mounds of New Madrid, Mo."); Mr. Auchincloss ("A monumental mass of Rock Salt"); Mr. Joseph W. Drexel, the banker, another early trustee ("2,235 specimens of Insects, Butterflies, Moths, etc.; Lot of Crustaceans, 4 Birds of Paradise, 3 Trogons, 16 South American Birds, 1 Rifle Bird, 1 Iguana, 1 Albino Squirrel, 3 Humming Birds"); Professor Marsh ("Cast of the left Femur of '*Atlantosaurus immanus*,' a Fossil Reptile from Colorado"); Sidney Dillon, president of the Union Pacific Railroad ("A Fossil Turtle from the Miocene of Colorado, and some Concretions from the same State"); Townsend Harris, the first American minister to Japan ("six specimens of Glass Rope Sponge, 1 Shark's Tooth"); and Professor Bickmore ("Knife and Scabbard and Arrow used by the Ainos, Island of Yesso")—and, more importantly, by the acquisition, for sixty-five thousand dollars, of what became known as the James Hall Collection of Invertebrate Fossils. This consisted of around one hundred thousand New York State and Middle Western specimens amassed by Mr. Hall, director of the New York State Museum in Albany.

In 1877, to sort these out, the Museum engaged its first curator—Robert P. Whitfield, a former Hall assistant and geology professor at Rensselaer Polytechnic Institute in Troy, who, during his thirty-two years as a quiet worker in the Manhattan Square attic, labeled, arranged, and installed them; wrote them up and drew pictures of their morphological structure in and for scores of scientific papers; and gave similar, loving attention to the rest of the Museum's rocky material. He also carried on a protracted, unloving correspondence with his former boss, who had fired him when Whitfield objected to Hall's taking his name off a lithological book that Whitfield had written (Hall, the founder of American stratigraphic geology, is described by Professor Nathan Reingold in his *Science in Nineteenth-Century America* as "an irascible, great figure in American geology"), and who, year after year, kept asking the Museum to return fossils that he said had been sent to it by mistake, or that he wanted for further study, or both. The feud may have been salubrious. Hall lived to be nearly eighty-eight, and Whitfield died a few weeks shy of his eighty-second birthday. "His associations with the objects that he loved, and which he conscientiously and unremittingly studied, remained unbroken to the end," the DAB says of him.

2

———————◆———————

D R. HOLDER, whose title was changed in 1881 from assistant superintendent to Curator of Zoology ("Holder was a high-minded man of wide culture," the DAB says of *him*) was the Museum's second full curator, but its second staff member to have the word "curator" in his official designation was Mr. Louis P. Gratacap, a modest individual, unsung in the encyclopedias, who has so captured my fancy that I propose to give him ample exhibition space. Born in Brooklyn in 1850, he graduated, at eighteen, from the Free Academy (now the City College), attended General Theological Seminary for two years as a candidate for the ministry of the Episcopal Church from the Diocese of New York, and then, changing his course, became a chemist for the Metropolitan Gas Light Company. On the side, he studied at the Columbia School of Mines (now the School of Engineering), where, in 1876, he received a Ph.B. Not a doctor. That fall, after writing Professor Bickmore for a part-time job ("I am

anxious to secure scientific employment and have begun
to search for it in various directions"), he began to sort
out mineralogical specimens, after hours, in the Arsenal,
of which he has written, in an unpublished history of the
Museum that sheds some light on the popularity of this
building as a Museum perch:

> The Arsenal was an inferior structure built about 1840 [Mr.
> Gratacap was wrong about this on all counts: the Arsenal,
> completed in 1848, is an excellent example of military architec-
> ture; it now houses the office of the Park Commissioner] and
> devoted to the use of an armory, later the temporary home
> of Menagerie animals. Odor of caged beasts clung to it. The
> Menagerie crowds swarmed through its halls after the Mu-
> seum got its second and third stories.

Gratacap left the gas-light business for full-time Museum employ in 1880, when he was appointed Assistant
Curator of Mineralogy. He later became Assistant Curator
of Geology and then Curator of Mineralogy and Mollusca.
(Mineralogy, originally under Professor Whitfield's Department of Geology, was raised to autonomy, and full
curatorship, in 1901, in order to take care of twelve
thousand minerals that J. P. Morgan had just bought from
Clarence S. Bement, a Philadelphia collector, and presented to the Museum. Its mysterious bracketing with
Mollusca may have been due to the fact that the Museum's
staff was small and that Mr. Gratacap was fond of shells.)
Gratacap's personality, and not a little of the Museum's
early history, are reflected in bundles of his interoffice
correspondence that are stuffed in steel cabinets in a win-
dowless dungeon in the Museum known as Central Files.
Many of these messages are addressed to Morris K. Jesup,
who became the Museum's third president in 1881, when

Mr. Stuart, who died the next year, resigned. Jesup, whom Gratacap outlived, served as president for twenty-seven years, giving the curator time to write him a great many letters.

GRATACAP TO JESUP, AUGUST 16, 1881.

In accordance with your implied wish I made a list of the duplicates at the arsenal and I am disappointed both in their number and appearance. . . . May I add that an almost indispensable requisite with our collection is a set of blow-pipe apparatus—many minerals *cannot* be determined by the eye only by reactions—the price is $30 or less.

The blowpipe was approved.

IDEM, NOVEMBER 12, 1883.

There are at present in the Museum about 3000 specimens of pressed plants and they are in danger of suffering complete ruin unless attended to. I am a member of the Torrey Botanical Club and a botanist of a little experience. . . . I wish to make the proposal . . . to take the folios *home* and work them over.

Whether or not this request was granted, the Museum's herbarium never got off the ground in anything but a literal sense. In 1891, when the New York Botanical Garden was founded, the Museum, at the suggestion of the City of New York (which was helping finance both institutions), got out of the botanical business and turned its plants over to the Garden. Botany survives at the Museum only in the Hall of Forestry, and, peripherally and unlabeled, in the background of some of the animal and ethnological display cases. There is no Curator of Botany.

IDEM, JUNE 26, 1886.

Mr. W. Wallace [William Wallace, the Museum's building superintendent] tells me that you were displeased at the throwing away of material from the Arsenal. I was requested to look after the cleaning out of the arsenal building, that the work should be done at once, that the Department of Parks was importunate, and needed the space. I went over and sent to the Museum *everything* that could be used for its purposes. I found a great quantity of useless iron ores which could be put to no possible use unless in an economic exhibit, and the localities had all disappeared from them. The rubbish represented all sorts of miscellaneous material brought from the [Philadelphia] Centennial which, had they been brought to the Museum, would only have been an aggravation and a ceaseless cause of annoyance. I . . . consulted Prof Bickmore who entirely approved of the work as I feel confident you would have had you seen the distressful collection of odds and ends which were disposed of.

IDEM, FEBRUARY 23, 1887.

I received your orders in reference to remaining at the Museum on Holidays. I certainly have not been at the Museum on those days in the past, and I never doubted the propriety of my conduct, as it was never questioned by those over me in the Museum.

IDEM, DECEMBER 20, 1888.

I should very much like to remain at home on Christmas Day . . .

Request granted.

IDEM, JANUARY 3, 1889.

I have this morning received your communication relative to the Evening Openings and some plan as to public instruction. . . . For myself I must beg you to excuse me from the performance of a work for which I have a profound distaste.

To teach a miscellaneous lot of careless men and women
with no real curiosity to know anything about the objects
they are shown; a sort of wandering caravan of stragglers
and the odds and ends of the streets, hustling through the
halls, is to me a dreary and repulsive business. . . . I believe
that all useful means for the education and gratification of
the public can be properly supplied by labels, guides, and
diagrams. . . . Labels and plenty of them are . . . needed.
Earnest and knowledge seeking people will learn more by
looking for themselves and asking questions than they can by
hearing an interrupted and vague talk. . . . The difficulties
are not inconsiderable to me, as I live out of New York and
would reach my home at or after Midnight. . . .

Gratacap, a lifelong bachelor, was living on Staten Island with his father and an invalid brother. His views
about public instruction were not shared by the management. Professor Bickmore had been giving lectures on
zoology to public-school teachers since 1880. In 1884, he
resigned as superintendent to become curator of a new
Department of Public Instruction, which drew on the Museum staff for its talkers and expanded the Museum audi-
ence to members, schoolchildren, and the general public.
It got to be supported by the state, which took over
Bickmore's salary. The Professor himself turned increasingly to such non-scientific lectures as "Germany—Berlin," "Holland—Amsterdam," "Belgium—Antwerp and
Bruges," "The Upper Rhine," "The Lower Rhine," "The
Swiss Alps," "The French Alps," and "The Adirondack
Park." "By the year 1904," the Museum's 1955 *Annual
Report* states in a retrospective essay, "[when] Bickmore's
failing health drew a halt to his museum career . . . the
program which he had started . . . had been extended to

over one million people, and his influence was widely felt
by teachers and students throughout the country."

GRATACAP TO JESUP, MARCH 11, 1890.

May I . . . earnestly request that the rule laid down for me
to be at the Museum at 9 o'clock A.M. be remitted. It is really
so unnecessary, and imposes upon me a hardship from which
no substantial benefits come to anyone. I leave my house
now at 8 A.M. and reach the Museum at 9:40 A.M. Can not
this continue?

It did.

GRATACAP TO WALLACE, MARCH 18, 1890.

I must attend the funeral of Judge Nehrbas *at 1 o'clock*.
He was my classmate.

No time to get in touch with Jesup in this emergency.

GRATACAP TO JESUP, NOVEMBER 5, 1890.

I am engaged upon a long and wearisome task; the making
of a Catalogue of all the Cabinet Fossils belonging to the
Museum. It would really assist me and certainly increase my
comfort considerably, if the Museum would furnish me a
reasonable and adequate chair. The perverse affair I use at
present is detestable. I am compelled to put a board on it
to use it at all, and it seems a fair and pertinent request to
ask for something like a rotatory office-chair which affords
its occupant some ease as well as assistance at his work.

Request granted.

IDEM, MAY 26, 1891.

I have been told by Prof. Bickmore, in a very accidental
sort of way, that I am expected to be here on Wednesday

evenings for the next four weeks. . . . If I am required to do
this skilled work of "projecting" on that evening (*sic*) . . .
may I make a very simple request? I do not ask for a pecuni-
ary remuneration, *although that would be much more acceptable,* but . . . will you allow me on these lecture days . . .
to come to the Museum at 3 P.M.?

This letter is signed "Yours respectfully," under which
Mr. Jesup has written, "Not after tonight." Gratacap's
chore was to handle the lantern slides for Bickmore's talks.
He eventually fell into line as a lecturer himself, and
gave a number of discourses on things like "New York
City, Past and Present," "The Parks of New York,"
"The Industries of the Sea," and "The Planets."

GRATACAP TO JOHN K. WINSER, SECRETARY OF THE MUSEUM,
OCTOBER 6, 1894.

I have a very little property—some few hundreds—which
I wish to protect. An election on Monday in which this
stock is concerned takes place at which it is indispensable I
should be present. The fight is a bitter one. I have joined the
opposition, and though I fear we will be beaten, every effort
we can make, will be made to upset the present management.

GRATACAP TO WHITFIELD, AUGUST 9, 1895, FROM CAPE BRETON,
NOVA SCOTIA.

This region is one of great interest. . . . The mountains
slope precipitously and plunge into the sea; at one famous
place—Cape Smoky—displaying great granitic faces of extraordinary dimensions. . . . The formations are carboniferous and
archaean. . . .

GRATACAP TO JESUP, FEBRUARY 1, 1896.

I beg to acknowledge the receipt of your letter, informing
me of my reengagement in the employ of the A.M.N.H. for

the ensuing year, and of the increase of my salary. This increase was certainly unexpected, but I can assure you it is
very welcome.

GRATACAP TO WHITFIELD, DECEMBER 2, 1896.

Please excuse my attendance at the Museum today. I'm
detained at home fighting or helping (I don't know which)
the furnace. We're just freezing here, and I want to see what
I can do.

GRATACAP TO WINSER, JANUARY 4, 1897.

I have been informed by an attendant that you inquired
for me on Sat. in the absence of Prof. W. and that I was
not here. I am not generally inclined to take blame I do
not deserve, but I think in this case I am censurable. The
insistency of friends, at whose house I was staying, overruled
my own better judgment and *inclination*.

GRATACAP TO JESUP, NOVEMBER 23, 1898.

I visited Mr. Kunz at Tiffany & Co., as you directed,
yesterday, and was shown the specimens you may contemplate
buying.
The Pyrite from Colorado (a mineral mass of yellow
crystals) for $30 is a beautiful and desirable thing. The price
is not excessive. The other mineral specimen, Wulfenite (a
mass of scarlet crystals), is also beautiful and desirable. It is
not dear. As to the two gems (one yellow beryl and one
quartz crystal, with some gold specimens), I am inclined to
think that at present they are not required. . . .

"Keep the Pyrite and Wulfenite," Mr. Jesup has written
on this letter. George Frederick Kunz, Tiffany's gem
expert and vice-president, made collections of gems for
J. P. Morgan which the latter gave to the Museum, of
which, in 1902, Kunz became Honorary Curator of Gems.

On February 24, 1899, in another letter to Mr. Jesup, Mr. Gratacap rose above departmental considerations and the exigencies of his personal life:

> In view of the apparent need of increasing the membership of the Museum, a return to the device practised ten years ago might prove serviceable. It was then customary to have two receptions a year, one in Spring and one in Autumn. These were made purely social occasions, and were limited to members and their friends. Some music was afforded, and previous to each reception the press of the city announced the new additions to the Museum, and gave to the reception a semi-fashionable interest.
>
> As society is generally most interested in doing what every one else is supposed to do, the fashionable world thus became partially involved in the maintenance of the Museum, not so much because it cared for the purposes of the Museum itself as because it was the right thing, Autumn and Spring, to attend its receptions. As a suggestion, a larger membership might, in this way, be secured.

The Museum had established a hierarchy of contributors at the outset—Patrons at twenty-five hundred dollars, Fellows in Perpetuity at a thousand dollars, Fellows for Life at five hundred dollars, Members for Life at two hundred and fifty dollars. These classifications, over the decades, have been revised downward and upward financially, and they have been added to and abolished—the Fellows in Perpetuity made an interesting disappearance many years ago. The 1960 *Annual Report* lists fourteen categories of paid memberships, ranging from a $2.50 Junior "Explorer" Membership to a $100,000 Endowment Member, and including a few semantic oddities. "Sustain" and "support" seem to mean the same thing in the dictionary, but in the Museum taxonomy Sustaining Members pay twenty-five dollars a year and Supporting Members, one hundred. And what are we to make of Associate Founders—individuals who have given the Museum twenty-five thousand dollars long after it was founded? Can a founder be retroactive? Well, no matter; in any event, a ten-dollar annual membership was set up in 1873. Its roster included William Waldorf and John Jacob Astor (who jumped to Fellow in Perpetuity the next year), P. T. Barnum, John C. Calhoun, twelve Colgates and six Roosevelts (of whom one in each family category was *also*, respectively, a Patron and a Fellow in Perpetuity), Whitelaw Reid, and Cyrus W. Field, who, in 1875, wrote Bickmore, "My dear Mr. Brickmore, I am unable to say at the moment whether I can go to the Park tomorrow. . . . I am very much occupied with important telegraph matters. I remain My dear Mr. Brickmore, Very truly your friend." Three years later, the layer of the Atlantic Cable climbed the ladder to Fellow in Perpetuity, and (despite this title) ended up a Patron. He may or may not have ever gained the Park, but he *did* get around. In 1892, the year of his death, he gave the Museum "one necklace of nuts and teeth, collected by him on the Andes, between Quito and Bogotá."

In 1899, when Mr. Gratacap made his psychological suggestion, the Museum had 458,451 visitors, among them Dr. A. B. Meyer, director of the Royal Zoological, Anthropological, and Ethnographical Museum of Dresden, who reported, in a book called *Über Museen des Ostens der Vereinigten Staaten von Amerika. Reisestudien,* which was translated into English and published by the Smithsonian Institution:

> . . . The American Museum of Natural History in New York is divided into 12 departments. The department of public instruction stands at the head of the list, a circumstance which indicates the main object of the museum. The director of this department (Bickmore) constantly keeps in stock, so to speak, 400 lectures on 200 different subjects. . . . The building . . . has a richly molded facade of red brick, syenite, and granite, with towers, jutties, balconies, roofs, etc., in modern Romanesque style, approaching the French castle type. . . . The value of the existing collections is estimated at $2,800,000. . . . The annual expenses of $136,000 are borne by the city. . . . In the year 1899, $48,000 additional was raised by private contribution. . . . For the increase of the collections, $95,000 is appropriated annually, including the cost of expeditions. . . . In 1899, the trustees expended $75,000 to make good a deficit caused by purchases. . . . In the year 1899 alone, Mr. Jesup gave $30,000 to the museum. . . .

Despite this flourishing picture, Gratacapiana indicates that the Museum was being run on a tight budget. On March 28, 1899, Gratacap wrote Secretary Winser, on the letterhead of Keeler's Hotel and Annex, Broadway & Maiden Lane, Albany, N.Y.:

> At Keeler's. Looks as if it would go off if you lit a match across the street. Shall sleep with my feet out of the window on the fire escape. Good for the Museum however—75 cts a day—for room—personal safety doesn't count.

The loyal curator had risked his life in order to look at some State Museum fossils the Museum was interested in. "Put in heavy day," he wrote the secretary the next day, "—from 9 to 5, hard at it, made 40 pages of notes, and inspected over 1000 drawers of fossils. I think I know pretty well what Hall has."

He found little solace back on Manhattan Square:

GRATACAP TO JESUP, MAY 10, 1899.

Prof. Whitfield has just told me that you desire the brass tacks which hold the shells in place [the writer had added mollusks to his responsibilities at this time] all removed and replaced by something else. This enormous and hurtful change is made I believe upon the utterly illusory and deceptive assumption that the tacks will corrode and spoil the shells. It is hard to restrain an exclamation of impatience at this unreasonable objection. These tacks will not corrode, they are not copper but brass, which, unless exposed to considerable moisture, a condition never existing in the halls, do not become coated with the green verdegris. It would almost seem as if this fictitious complaint was raised for the purpose of embarrassing and disparaging me. . . . I was stupefied at such an unreasonable and unwelcome statement. . . . To remove these tacks after all the careful labor expended on the installation for so baseless an objection does seem to me a most unjust exaction.

Again Prof. Whitfield tells me that you object to the removal of the *Economic Series* to make room for the minerals. I did this . . . for the best interests of the Museum. If you will examine the situation yourself, you will see how inharmonious it would be to interrupt an exhibit of the Wall Case specimens of the Mineral Cabinet . . . by this straggling show of a few ores and clays. . . . I have worked undeviatingly for the interests of the public, and it is humiliating to be condemned unheard, and unsupported. I feel as if it were best for me to resign, and I shall be very glad to accept your assistance in securing a position elsewhere, amid more friendly associations, if possible.

Mr. Jesup overruled Mr. Gratacap's objections, but the assistant curator remained at his post.

GRATACAP TO WINSER, JANUARY 3, 1900.

I have been absent from the Museum the last two Saturdays. The end of the year finds me now, at each return, unfortunately involved in some financial trouble. This occasionally compels my absence during a day or so in December. I wish also next Saturday afternoon to entertain two young friends, as a kind of Xmas gift. With this, my omissions of attendance cease.

His relations with the president soon improved:

GRATACAP TO JESUP, NOVEMBER 14, 1900.

A chance remark of yours in reference to the indifference of the public to the shells affords me the opportunity to say that this is largely due to the fact that they have only Latin names which no one comprehends. I have often thought if the . . . common name was given them, together with the Latin name, people would inspect them more attentively.

"I fully endorse this," Mr. Jesup wrote on the back of this communication. "It is well known how I have struggled with the Prof [Whitfield] about labels." A few weeks later, he raised Gratacap to full curatorship.

IDEM, JANUARY 2, 1901.

The information from yourself that I have been appointed Curator of the Department of Mineralogy, and in charge of Conchology, gives me a serious sense of responsibility. . . . Thanking you for what is to me a really unexpected honor, I remain, in the spirit of the New Year, yours respectfully.

Trouble lay ahead, however. In a letter simply dated 1902, with no month or day, an omission perhaps caused by agitation, the new Curator of Minerals wrote Dr. Hermon C. Bumpus, then the Museum's director:

> It is with the greatest solicitude that I am compelled to report the unaccountable disappearance of 13 entries of the Meteoric specimens catalogued in the old collection. . . . It always seemed to me that something more secure and heavy than the flimsy locks at present on the *old* cases was necessary.

And on December 8, 1904, he wrote the director:

> I have just made the staggering and distressing discovery that thieves have been at work in this Department. They have ransacked the Bement Golds and have even reached the gold in the Gem Collection. The work has been done with exacting pains. Not a tray is absent from the case where the Bement golds are exhibited. Specimens, of a poor quality, have been . . .

The Bement Golds were part of Mr. Morgan's gift; the Gem Collection consisted largely of the Tiffany Company exhibits at the Paris Expositions of 1889 and 1900, which Morgan had also bought for the Museum. The rest of the letter about their looting appears to be missing from Central Files, but a May 27, 1902, Gratacap-to-Bumpus communication is on hand, and may be adduced as an example of a kind of curatorial frustration that is as common today as it was then:

> After a trying encounter with the stupidity and indirection of the L.Is.R.R. I reached the village of Hollis, saw the "aged German" and the missive from Martinique. The former

is a humbug, also the latter. The "meteoric stranger" is a good sized trap fragment, water worn and encrusted with dirt, and has been taken out of a hole just about large enough to admit of its adroit insertion. It was a disappointment, and I declined to leave any consideration for the pleasure of seeing it.

Further light on Mr. Gratacap's activities is shed by three Centrally Filed communications, the first of which, dated March 15, 1908, is marked "Referred to Mr. Gratacap for reply."

DEAR SIR: I am a little boy of Newark New Jersey, and am interested in rocks and stones and making a collection of my own. I wonder whether at the Mus. you have duplicates or inferior specimens that you will dispose of at reasonable prices. If so, will you please name the specimens and prices and I will arrange to come over soon to examine them.

Yours truly,
R. GORDON WASSON.

This was followed by two undated letters, the first signed by Thomas C. Wasson and R. Gordon Wasson, and the second by R. Gordon Wasson alone:

Mr. L. P. Getacap, My dear Sir: As we are going to the country during our vacation, and you asked us not to come to the Museum on a Saturday (*vide supra*), we shall come up after school some day this week, probably Thursday or Friday.

My Dear Mr. L. P. Gratacap: My dear Sir. Thank you very much for your kind offer. I will come the first day of my spring vacation, in about two weeks. My older brother, 12 years old, will come with me. We have everything in partnership. We have not got many rocks, so we shall be glad to get any.

The younger Wasson, who was nine, grew up to be a vice-president of J. P. Morgan & Co. and an authority on mushrooms. In 1957, he and his wife, who was born in St. Petersburg, wrote and produced a wonderfully illustrated two-volume book, *Mushrooms, Russia and History*, which, issued in an edition of five hundred copies, sold for one hundred and twenty-five dollars a set. The Museum used this work as the generating feature of a temporary show exhibiting the hallucinogenic mushrooms of Mexico, a Wasson specialty. A contemporary student of the Museum ran into Mr. Wasson soon after running into his letters. "I remember the sequel well," he said. "Tom and I planned the solicitation, but he, perhaps fearing a brush-off, put his younger brother up to initiating the correspondence. We turned up on the appointed day, and Mr. Gratacap showed us over the mineral collections and explained things to us. He gave us, of course without charge, from the cellar, as much in the way of diversified specimens as we could carry, which, considering our appetite, was plenty. I remember going out of my mind with impatience as he meticulously labeled each stone with its Latin name. He also admonished us, with an emphasis that is still graven on my memory, how *not* to make a collection of stones. One does not solicit stones from a museum. One makes field trips and discovers the stones in their natural habitat."

Mr. Wasson is the publisher of another limited-edition book, *That Gettysburg Address*, issued in 1965, which contains an essay by his father, the Rev. Edmund Atwill Wasson, in which the author takes the Address apart and rewrites it. This exercise is followed by a less pejorative

"Postscriptum: A Memoir," wherein the son pays affectionate tribute to his father and goes on:

> . . . Before we were ten years old our father would send us perhaps once a month, on a Saturday, to New York, lunch baskets under our arms. Businessmen, regular commuters, were sometimes startled to see two little urchins—the Wasson boys! —going in on the train with them. We would visit the Aquarium and St. Paul's Chapel one day, the Metropolitan Museum on yet another, but our own favorite was the Natural History Museum, as this institution was commonly called. How its rich collections excited our imagination! And afterwards there were always the inviting grounds on which to eat our lunch, in the shade of the lofty trees with the Ninth Avenue El roaring by.

As for Thomas Wasson, he joined the Foreign Service in the middle 1920s. In 1948, when he was consul general in Jerusalem, he was shot to death in the street during an Arab-Jewish fight as he was returning from a meeting of a three-man truce commission representing the United Nations.

Children's letters do not abound in the Museum's files, but these *do* contain one from a distinguished *thirteen-*year-old, dated March 14, 1895:

> I beg to acknowledge my Life Membership ticket which I received this morning. I was about to notify you that I had lost it, when it arrived.
>
> *Yours sincerely,*
> FRANKLIN D. ROOSEVELT

The new Life Member, whose ticket, a Christmas present from his maternal grandfather, Warren Delano, got him into a group that included the painters Frederick E.

Church and Charles Moran and the bankers Henry Clews and Jacob H. Schiff, promptly gave the Museum "1 Vireo's Nest." Two years later, he contributed ten Pine Grosbeaks, and thirty-nine years after *that*, as President of the United States, he delivered the opening speech at the dedication of the Roman Eclectic Memorial Building to his presidential cousin.

Mr. Gratacap's chief epistolary target, Mr. Jesup, had died a few weeks before the Wassons' visit, and Henry Fairfield Osborn, the Museum's next president, did not take his place as a Gratacap confidant. In the fall of 1908, he moved Gratacap and his minerals out of their hall (into a gallery) to make room for the growing Department of Vertebrate Paleontology, which was Osborn's particular Museum baby, and in 1910 Mr. George H. Sherwood, the Museum's assistant secretary, wrote the Curator of Mineralogy and Conchology:

> The President has requested me to call the attention of the heads of departments to the regulation of the Museum providing that copies of all the official correspondence of the Curators shall be filed in the Director's Office, and he desires to have the provisions of this regulation strictly adhered to.

Gratacap was in the habit of writing in longhand, in ink, and this regulation may have cramped his style. Nor, as a writer of chatty notes to the president, can he have been encouraged by a November 28, 1910, communication from Osborn which began, "The most difficult scientific writing in the world is that of a Label. Kindly try again." In 1917, however, he sent a letter (painfully typed) to Dr. Frederic A. Lucas, who had succeeded Dr. Bumpus as director, which suggests that the veteran mineralogist and conchologist had not lost his spirit:

> I shall be very glad to do what I can in installing the [shell] Collection. . . . If the exhibit is to be made in the Hall of Vertebrate Palaeontology, I very earnestly crave full protection against a personal assault from Matthew.

To appreciate this allusion, we must jump around a bit, chronologically. Dr. William D. Matthew, the man who scared Gratacap, was a vertebrate paleontologist whom Osborn brought to the Museum in 1895, a few years after he had founded the Department of Vertebrate Paleontology there. At the time of Gratacap's fright, Matthew was an assistant in the department; in 1911, he became its curator. During his thirty-two years at the Museum (he resigned in 1927 to join the faculty of the University of California), he collected a great many bones in the Rocky Mountain area and published two hundred and forty papers with titles like "A Fossil Hedgehog from the American Oligocene," "A Horned Rodent from the Colorado Miocene. With a Revision of the Mylagauli, Beavers, and Hares of the American Tertiary," "Is the White River Tertiary an Eolian Formation?", and "On the Osteology and Relationships of *Paramys*, and the Affinities of the Ischyromyidae." His *chef-d'oeuvre* was *Climate and Evolution*, of which the DAB writes:

> . . . In [it] he argued for the relative permanency of the great ocean basins and the continental masses, and against the existence of former land bridges across what are now abyssal depths. The population by terrestrial mammals of such islands as Cuba he attributed to transportation by means

of natural rafts. One of the main theses of this important
contribution to science was that the majority of the orders
and families of mammals had their origin in the Northern
Hemisphere, subsequently spreading to southern areas, and
that long isolation in the more remote southern areas, such
as Australia, accounted for the extraordinary primitive faunas
found there.

The *Museologist*, an intramural Museum magazine
which was published, briefly, in the early 1920s, treated
Dr. Matthew and his theories in a lighter vein:

> We once did know an F.R.S. [Fellow of the Royal Society]
>   named Matthew, William Diller,
> Of palaeontology a prop, of society a pillar.
> But theories weird of natural rafts obsessed this mighty
>   scholar,
> To hint that beasts could *walk* across made him warm be-
>   neath the collar.
>
> Now everywhere that William went his wife was sure to
>   foller—
> "Whither thou goest I will go if it takes my bottom dollar.
> "You cannot treat me like a worm or humble caterpillar,
> "I'll string along with you, my dear," said Matthew, Kitty
>   Diller.
>
> "You know full well that far from you my joy would be but
>   holler,
> "So pack your bag, we'll blithely go and heed nor *sou* nor
>   *thaler*.
> "With me you need not fear to sail upon the rolling biller."
> "But I wish there *were* a land bridge," sighed Matthew,
>   William Diller.

It will, perhaps, come as a surprise to no one who has
strung along with Mr. Gratacap's correspondence to learn
that he did not confine his literary efforts to interoffice

communication and an unpublished history of the Museum.
Beginning in 1887, he wrote twenty or thirty books and
pamphlets, some of which also had pretty catchy titles—
"Philosophy of Ritualism, or Apologia pro Ritu," "Ana-
lytics of a Belief in a Future State," *The Power of Silence,
Why the Democrats Must Go, Europe's Handicap, The
Mayor of New York: A Romance of Days to Come,
Benjamin the Jew, A Woman of the Ice Age, The Cer-
tainty of a Future Life in Mars,* and "As to the Public
Schools." *The Mayor* and *Benjamin* were rather sensational
novels about life in New York and Newport; the Ice Age
and Mars books were science fiction. The latter, subtitled "Being the Posthumous Papers of Bradford Torrey
Dodd. Edited by L. P. Gratacap," is an account of Mr.
Dodd's correspondence, via wireless, with his deceased
father, who, transmogrified and reborn, has settled on
Mars. There, among other sights, he describes his visit to
a huge dining room, where, at one of the tables, he
catches a glimpse of Dalton, Berzelius, Lavoisier, Faraday,
Volta, Fahrenheit, and Joseph Henry. (Only consequential corpses were admitted to the Dodd-Gratacap planet.)
The Museum of Natural History, which has not stocked
many of Mr. Gratacap's books, has taken this one at its
title face value. It catalogues it in its library as a work
edited by Gratacap, and keeps a copy in the astronomical
library of the Hayden Planetarium.

In *A Woman of the Ice Age,* published in 1906,
shortly after its author had returned from Museum expeditions to Newfoundland and Iceland with a bag of
beetles, mollusks, zeolites, and Ordovician fossils, a woman
named Lhatto falls in love with a man named Ogga.

She raised her hands as if in oblation to the light above her, her tumultuous black hair streamed down her naked back, and she sighed [the author writes, in part]. The poise was perfect, the aesthetic unity complete. Gold bands held her ankles, gold links were upon her wrists and ears, a white shell comb was inserted in her hair, and an apron of fox skin hung before her. Such was Lhatto, the girl of the Sierras, before human history began, the Woman of the Ice Age, living in the warm Fair Land in North America.

Lhatto walks to the ocean, gets into a canoe, and presently falls asleep.

Where the opening valleys of the Fair Land turned northward into the Dismal Country of heaped ridges, interminable peat bogs, low woods, and scanty or puissant streams [the author continues], upon an upland sparingly covered with trees . . . dwelt Ogga—the mastodon hunter.

Ogga sings "the song of the mastodon," and also walks to the ocean.

His eyes, bright with ardor and delight, sought out the line of pale icebergs, and then they fell below him upon the transparent and liquid beryl lapping languorously at his feet. And as they fell, upon their retinas sprang the image fair and true, of a sleeping woman's face, dark and beautiful, amid dishevelled hair, rocking in a little boat, as in a cradle, on the quietly heaving bosom of the sea. It was Lhatto. . . . As Ogga saw Lhatto, he loved her, and he loved her nobly. The whole process of approach, preparation, attack and capture was instantaneously traversed. How could it be otherwise! The physiological instant was critical and victorious.

After many adventures, as the Ice Age recedes, the lovers die on a desert. The book, which concludes, rather mysteriously, "So, in the far backward of time, as the Ice Age departed, the Man and Woman began the endless Poem of Life, endlessly beautiful, endlessly sad," contains a reference to a former Gratacap colleague, Dr. Jacob L. Wortman, like Dr. Matthew an Osborn recruit to Vertebrate Paleontology. (He left in 1899 to go to the Carnegie Museum in Pittsburgh.) Dr. Wortman is brought into the prehistoric picture when Ogga encounters a "gigantic sloth, the relative of the megatherium and mylodon, the excrescent development of that group of animals which typify to the psychologist the inertia of mind and the collapse of invention, the drugged dyspeptic sleep of creation and creators":

> Now, as a matter of more discreet scientific statement, the world of science has almost resolved, after some remarkable demonstrations of Dr. J. L. Wortman, to believe that the great South American family of the sloths (*Tardigrades*) originated in the North American continent, that they issued from the family of the *Ganodonta*. It seems certain . . .

(Cf. "The Ganodonta and their Relationship to the Edentata," Wortman, *Bulletin of the American Museum of Natural History*, 1897. But cf., also, *O. C. Marsh: Pioneer in Paleontology*, by Charles Schuchert and Clara Mae LeVene, 1940: "Wortman agreed with Marsh . . . that this great group of peculiar mammals originated in North America and then migrated to other parts of the world. This is not, however, the view of present-day students of fossil edentates. . . ." It is a matter of regret in the world of science that Wortman, after a jurisdictional row, resigned from the Carnegie Museum, after only one year there, and, with twenty-six years to go, according to an obituary published in this outfit's *Annals*, "literally 'shook the dust' of paleontology from his feet . . . and absolutely refused even to read anything relating to the science in which he had already achieved for himself an enduring reputation.")

Back to Gratacap. In *The Mayor of New York*, whose "Days to Come" action starts in the year 2000, the author pays tribute to the man who gave him his rotatory office chair.

> As early as the end of the nineteenth century a few rich men had begun a process of self-appraisement and conciliation. Rockefeller, Carnegie, Stanford, Widener, Mills, Morgan, Jesup and others had signalized their oneness with the great majority, and their personal sense of responsibility, by large gifts to the common weal. . . . They established a certain nobility of conduct, as essential to wealth.

The book has a rich, noble heroine, Helen Lorimer, whose dream is to move the Pope to America—thus getting him out of the miserable, caste-ridden continent of Europe, which Gratacap detested. (Cf. *Europe's Handicap*.) Miss Lorimer's dream comes true: the novel ends with the resettling of the Holy See in Gratacap's home base, Staten Island, and the installation of the Pope in a house she has paid for.

Gratacap, whose middle name, incidentally, was Pope, was a handsome man with a flourishing mustache and head of hair. He was given to high black shoes, four-button suits, and polka-dot ties. Much in demand as a speaker at class reunions, he resisted efforts that were made to turn

him into a professional lecturer. "He hid his light beneath his collection cases," a friend has written. His books
failed to make him rich—"We will endeavor to sell these,"
Brentano's wrote him of a remainder of the one on Mars,
which it had published, "as you suggest, at 10¢ per volume,
the proceeds to be divided equally between Brentano's
and yourself"—and he attached little importance to
money. In 1915, when the Museum trustees voted him a
six months' leave of absence at full pay and five hundred
dollars for traveling expenses, he expressed "some doubt
as to the propriety of my acceptance of a gift so munifi-
cent." He died two years later, and was buried in a family
vault in Trinity Church. After his death, Dr. Lucas wrote:

> Mr. Gratacap was of French descent, and his precise and
> somewhat formal mode of speech and courteous manner ever
> carried with them the suggestion of a gentleman of the old
> school. . . . He was . . . almost the only man to my knowl-
> edge who ever expressed himself as considering his services
> properly remunerated.

3

MORRIS K. JESUP, the man who put the Museum on its feet (its attendance was so discouraging when he took over, in 1881, that the trustees had seriously considered winding the place up), had to put himself on his feet first. He was born in Connecticut of pious New England stock, the son of an American Tract Society-backing businessman who died, broke, during the panic of 1837. Morris and his seven brothers and sisters were brought up in New York by their widowed mother, who had, luckily, a solvent father-in-law, and whose "brave efforts, with slender resources, to hold the family together until the children could become self-supporting" have been noted by the DAB. At twelve, Morris quit school to go to work as an errand boy for Rogers, Ketchum & Grosvenor, a Wall Street firm of manufacturers of locomotives and cotton-mill machinery (later the Rogers Locomotive Works) whose factory was in Paterson, New Jersey. Ac-

cording to his biographer, the Rev. William Adams Brown
(the son of a Brown Brothers Brown who also wrote
books called *The Essence of Christianity* and *God at
Work*), he often got up at four in the morning to attend
to the loading of locomotive parts on freight cars. At
twenty-four, when he was making six hundred dollars a
year as chief clerk, he resigned and went into business
with a friend, selling railroad supplies on commission. He
soon graduated into merchant banking, specializing in railroad securities. His clients included the Chicago & Alton
Railroad, the Southern Railroad, the Atlantic Coast Line,
Joseph W. Drexel, and the Gaekwar of Baroda. By the
time he joined the Museum's incorporators, in 1868,
he was a full-fledged multimillionaire and philanthropist
("Giving should be a habit with all Christian men and
women, as much as praying or eating," he once said.
"With the habit thus formed, life can be made happy,
dignified, and joyous"); he had a full-fledged, dignified
set of whiskers; so great were the demands made on him
that his letterhead bore the legend "Business Transacted
at Office Only." He retired from active business three
years after becoming the Museum's president. Jesup was
a multiple president. He held this title, at various times,
with the Five Points House of Industry, a "Home for
Homeless Children"; Sailors' Snug Harbor (a home for
homeless sailors); the Audubon Society of the State of
New York; the New York City Chamber of Commerce;
the New York City Mission and Tract Society; the American Sunday School Union; and the Syrian Protestant
College of Beirut. He was also an incorporator of the

New York Botanical Garden and an officer or trustee of the John F. Slater Fund and the Peabody Education Fund (both of which promoted post-Civil War Negro education in the South), the Society for Relief of Half-Orphan and Destitute Children, the New York Institution for the Deaf and Dumb, the Society for the Suppression of Vice, the New York Zoological Society, and the A.S.P.C.A. Although a 1902 article about the Museum in *Le Petit Temps*, a Paris newspaper, referred to him as "M. Jesup, riche financier israélite," he was, in fact (along with his Mission and Tract, Sunday School, and Beirut posts), a founder of the Presbyterian Hospital and the Y.M.C.A., and a trustee of Union Theological Seminary and the Brick Presbyterian Church. He thus exemplified, in a rather pure form, the pattern of the Museum's early trustees (which survives to a considerable extent in their successors today) of a man more widely concerned with good works than with scientific works.

Jesup liked trees, more for their economic usefulness than anything else, and this got him, and the Museum, into dendrology. He founded a Department of Economic Botany (later called the Department of Woods and Forestry), whose central feature was a collection forthrightly called North American Woods, on which, over a period of twenty or thirty years, he spent, out of his own pocket, something like a hundred thousand dollars—chiefly for the salaries of field collectors and Professor Charles S. Sargent, the director of the Arnold Arboretum, in Cambridge, Massachusetts, who moonlighted as Economic Botany's director. "Specimens . . . of all the woods of

our country, that are or may be used for architectural
or building purposes, or in the manufactures—as gums,
resins, and dyewoods," an early *Annual Report* said of
this collection. "Each species will be fully illustrated by
specimens of the leaf, flower, and fruit." As a corollary,
Jesup formed a Collection of Economic Entomology, em-
bracing insects that were natural enemies of trees. He
himself was a natural enemy of snakes. He realized that
snakes were part of natural history, and he did not proclaim the Museum out of bounds for these reptiles, but
they received a low rating during his tenure. On the
curatorial side, they went unrecognized until the year
after his death, when a Department of Ichthyology and
Herpetology was set up, with Bashford Dean, a Columbia
professor who was a straight fish-and-crustacean man in
the field of zoology, in charge. (Fascinated alike by the
carapace of the lobster and the shield of the medieval
knight, Dean was also Curator of Arms and Armor at
the Metropolitan Museum of Art.) "You have the starting of an excellent reptile collection in your Museum,"
Thomas Barbour, the Boston naturalist, wrote President
Osborn in 1910, but he went on to say, "It is in a very
chaotic state." It was not until 1920, twelve years after
Jesup's death, that a separate Department of Herpetology
was established, and it was not until 1942 that this department, lagging behind every other zoological subdivi-
sion of the Museum, had more than one curator on its
staff (two). (What would Mr. Jesup have said to the
present director, Dr. James A. Oliver, an enthusiastic herpetologist, author of *Snakes in Fact and Fiction*, who

was once in charge of the reptile house at the Bronx Zoo and who until recently kept a live rattlesnake in his office at the Museum! This snake, a relatively rare one —*Crotalus lepidus*, popularly known as a green rock rattler—was captured in 1963 in Colorado by the director's son, Dexter. For several years, Dr. Oliver fed it a white mouse every other Wednesday. "We used to feed it on Friday," Miss Wendy Wood, the director's secretary, once said, "but we changed to Wednesday in case of indigestion. We wouldn't want the snake to be sick over the weekend, when the office is generally closed." Crotalus died in the summer of 1967, and was succeeded by a rubber boa from Oregon—*Charina bottae*—which Vincent D. Roth, resident director of the Museum's Southwestern Research Station, sent to Dr. Oliver to make him feel better. The Museum's director also shares his working quarters with an Egyptian lizard—*Uromastix acanthinurus*, popularly known as Bell's Dabb Lizard—whom Miss Wood plies with iceberg lettuce from the staff cafeteria.)

Jesup's general orientation as a museum man has been summed up in a characterization by Dr. Bumpus:

> It was a fortunate thing that . . . the newly elected President, although in sympathy with science, had received no scientific training. He began his duties untrammeled by tradition. He was the advocate of no established school or method; his desire was merely that the Museum should be financially sound; that established business methods should obtain, and that the institution should actively minister to the people of the city. The impelling motive of his entire administration was the desire that the Museum should be instructive.

And in another, by the Rev. Brown:

> He wished . . . to make [the Museum] first as an agency of
> popular instruction, and nothing delighted him more than to
> see its rooms thronged with working men and children from
> the tenements studying the labels which set forth in simple
> language the nature of the objects which the cases contained.

The Museum, in turn, early on, set forth in simple
language the nature of its gratitude toward its president.
The first issue of its *Bulletin*, in 1881, starts off with a
description by Professor Whitfield of a new species of
crinoid from the Burlington limestone, at Burlington, Iowa,
appropriately named *Poteriocrinus Jesupi*. "The specific
name is given in honor of Morris K. Jesup, Esq., President
of the Am. Mus. of Nat. Hist.," Dr. Whitfield wrote,
"through whose liberality the collection of which it
forms a part was secured to the Museum."

The Am. Mus. of Nat. Hist. was by all odds Jesup's
favorite institution. He gave it four hundred and fifty
thousand dollars outright during his lifetime, and he left
it a million dollars in trust at his death. The Jesups had
no children. When Mrs. Jesup died, six years later, she
left the Museum, also in trust, nearly five million dollars
out of a twelve-million-dollar estate inherited from her
husband—in this way following rather closely an "If-I-
shall-survive-my-wife" residuary-estate bequest in his will
which had put the Museum down for 89/200ths of around
ten million dollars. The Jesup fund now amounts to ten
and a half million dollars, and thus constitutes around one-
fifth of the Museum's total endowment.

Mr. Jesup's will was cosier than most such documents are today. "Since [becoming the Museum's president] I have devoted a great part of my life, my time, my thoughts, and my attention to its interests," it stated. "I believe it to be today one of the most effective agencies which exist in the City of New York for furnishing education, innocent amusement, and instruction to the people." The testator spent several days a week in his office in the Museum. The nature and extent of his devotion to this innocent attraction are revealed in a voluminous correspondence, much of it intramural, that passed over his desk; the Gratacap letters are a mere trickle in this river. In the good old days of the nineteenth century, everyone from the night watchman up felt free to write the president. He went over their messages with the Museum's secretary, and annotated many of them, and their envelopes, indicating his reaction, in ink, pencil, or colored crayon, in a decisive, slanting hand. From a Central Files inspection of this material, there emerges a picture of presidential attention to detail and a remarkable range of direct solicitude. Herewith some extracts, arranged more or less chronologically, along with a few post-Jesup annotations, glosses, and digressions.

JOEL A. ALLEN, CURATOR OF ORNITHOLOGY AND MAMMALOGY FROM 1885 TO 1921, TO JESUP, JULY 13, 1885.

I very much wish that storage cases could be built against the walls of Room Z, for the reception of skulls and skeletons. At present they are piled up in trays, practically inaccessible, and exposed to injury from dust and other causes. (Marked "Approved.")

IDEM, JANUARY 1, 1887.

Prof. Ward has just informed me that his son has just returned from a trip to the Gulf of Mexico for a rare species of North American Seal. . . . He has been very successful, being able to bring back with him quite a number of specimens. This Seal is the rarest and least known of all the Seals. . . . We now have the opportunity to secure an adult male and female, and a young one, and a skeleton. The price for the first three is $250, or, with the skeleton—making four specimens—$325. . . . Here is a chance to work up one of the most interesting questions in Mammalogy. . . . It would make a very important paper for the Museum *Bulletin*. . . . The present case is an *emergency*—an *opportunity*, for me and the Museum, such as occurs but a few times in one's lifetime.

Henry A. Ward was a naturalist who had studied and worked with Agassiz at Cambridge, taught natural science at the University of Rochester, and founded, in Rochester, Ward's Natural Science Establishment, which sold specimens to museums and colleges, and trained taxidermists, several of whom—Dr. Lucas was one—later rose high in the *Museum* Establishment.

J. J. BARGIN, THE MUSEUM'S ASSISTANT SECRETARY, TO JESUP, AUGUST 20, 1885.

As I intimated to you some months ago, I find it impossible to support myself and family in a respectable manner on my present salary. . . . Such being the case, I am compelled to seek more lucrative employment elsewhere. . . . I return with my family to Scotland and should deem it a kindness to be released on the first of September in order that we may cross the Atlantic before bad weather sets in.

Mr. Bargin, who had presented the Museum with a hornets' nest in 1875, when he was a ten-dollar-a-week clerk on the staff, was released. A letter dated June 26, 1900, unsigned but in his handwriting, and apparently delivered by hand (it is addressed in an unstamped envelope to William Wallace, the building superintendent), hints at a sad sequel:

> You will remember Bargin, who was associated with you in the Office Work of the Museum 14 years ago. He has returned, and if you are still friendly to him, is anxious to meet you to learn something of his Mother, Wife and child. Will you kindly meet him at your earliest convenience this afternoon at the entrance to the Park opposite the Museum at 77th and 8th Ave. where he will be waiting, and a preliminary interview take place without anyone knowing it, for the present.
>
> If you are still well disposed to him, kindly give a sign of it by waving your hand or handkerchief in advance that he may know that he can still trust you of yore. If he does not see this sign in the distance as you approach he will understand that all is over and turn the other way.
>
> *Yours truly,*
>
> ONE WHO KNOWS OF BARGIN'S CREDITABLE CAREER SINCE HE LEFT N.Y. AND IS ANXIOUS TO NOW RETURN TO THE MUSEUM, IF IT IS POSSIBLE.

A final sentence revealed the writer's identity: "If you are not in the Museum this afternoon I will call again tomorrow a.m. bet 9 & 10 o'clock at the same meeting place."

PERCY R. PYNE, A MUSEUM TRUSTEE SINCE 1872, TO JESUP, 1885.

> The birds at the Smithsonian do not appear to anything like the same advantage as ours. Their mammals (except in skeletons) amount to nothing at all.

The Museum at this time had ten thousand stuffed birds and three thousand skins. Its mammals included the finest series of monkeys of the world in American hands (bought from Ward); a mounted caribou given to it by Albert Bierstadt, the landscape painter, who had just begun to portray wild animals as well; and a Rocky Mountain goat, from Mr. Pyne. The latter was not alone in his ornithological opinion. The year before, in the *Annual Report* of the Smithsonian Institution, Mr. Robert Ridgway, the Smithsonian's Curator of Birds, after complaining about his cases, had written:

> The American Museum . . . is able, on account of its large, well-lighted, and admirably constructed cases, to make a display of the most diversified forms of the feathered creation, with which the bird exhibit of the National Museum cannot be compared, except to its discredit. . . . During a recent inspection of the Museum in New York City, the curator made a list of more than 100 species of foreign birds which constitute the chief attraction of that superb museum, all of which are wanting to the national collection.

For all its birdy advantages, the New York museum deferred, in a birdy way, to Washington; shortly after Mr. Ridgway's bow, it sent one hundred forms of the feathered creation to the Smithsonian "for determination."

SPENCER F. BAIRD, SECRETARY OF THE SMITHSONIAN, TO JESUP, JANUARY 16, 1886.

> I beg to call your attention to the fact that the offer of the Smithsonian Institution to supply the American Museum . . . with some of its duplicates of fish casts has not yet been formally acknowledged or accepted. If, as I gathered during your recent visit to Washington, you desire to receive these objects . . . I shall be pleased to have a specific statement to that effect.

The casts were accepted; they constituted one of a long series of gifts or exchanges—often of duplicates—between the two repositories. In 1880, for example, the American Museum had sent some Hall fossil duplicates to the Smithsonian; others were sold to Madison University. And two or three years after Baird's fish-casts present, his assistant secretary, Dr. George Brown Goode, wrote Jesup:

> I desire to acknowledge the receipt of a skin of Bull Moose, a skin of African Lion, and two skins of prong-horned Antelopes. . . . I now take pleasure in informing you of the transmission this day, by freight, to the American Museum of Natural History, of a wet skin of a bull Buffalo.

The Museum and the Smithsonian also exchanged *information*. Most of this was scientific, but some of it was empirical. In 1870, Mr. William Haines, a Museum vice-president, consulted Spencer Baird as to the depth of his wall cases, and in 1875 Baird asked the Museum for a set of photographs of its building "so that I may have a chance of studying up the many excellent features of its construction." In 1908, the assistant secretary of the Smithsonian, Mr. Richard Rathbun, sought the advice of the Museum's director, Dr. Bumpus, on a matter that was, again, connected, in a way, with wet skins:

> I write to ask . . . whether it is the custom in your Museum to collect from visitors' umbrellas, canes, and other packages (*sic*) when entering the building, and if the package is lost, whether the Museum holds itself responsible for the same, and pays the owner. Our custom here had been to hold the watchmen responsible when he (*sic*) cannot produce the article checked, but we have recently had two cases where the visitor

declined to receive the umbrella on the ground that they (sic) had deposited a very much better article, and demanded payment for the same. This is manifestly unfair to the watchmen, as you can readily see that any unprincipled person could work off old umbrellas for new ones without the slightest trouble. . . .

The Museum replied that it checked packages but not canes or umbrellas, except on request, and that this policy (which has since been changed) had got it into trouble only once or twice in the preceding six or seven years. The Smithsonian replied that it proposed to follow suit.

The Museum, moving with the alacrity of a private institution, sometimes got ahead of the Smithsonian when it came to acquiring specimens:

WILLIAM A. WALLACE TO JESUP, JUNE 28, 1886.

The skeleton and skin of the Rhinoceros will cost one hundred and fifty dollars. Prof. Ward is trying to get it and Mr. Richardson tells me that if the Smithsonian Institution hears about it, that (sic) they will make a much larger offer for it.

Mr. Allen is more than pleased to think that you secure both skin and skeleton for the Museum.

The Park Department had to move the skeleton and I asked Mr. Conklin to let it come here and he could move it from here if you did not approve of its purchase.

Jenness Richardson, newly enticed from Smithsonian employ by Dr. Allen, was the Museum's first staff taxidermist; William C. Conklin was superintendent of the Central Park Menagerie, the source of the skeleton. "I am glad the skeleton and bones (sic) are at our Museum," Mr. Jesup wrote on the back of the building superintendent's note. "You see Mr. Conklin & say I will see him tomorrow about the skin. Ask Mr. Richardson if he can stuff & mount the animal & come to my house this evening about 6 o c and see me."

ELLIOTT F. SHEPARD TO JESUP, NOVEMBER 22, 1887.

When in the Yellowstone National Park in September last, I procured some of the material from one of the so-called "Paint Pots" in the Lower Geyser Basin, where it continually boils, seethes, and bubbles, and I beg you to send for the Museum, a can of the curious substance.

Colonel Shepard, proprietor of the *Evening Mail and Express,* was a son-in-law of William H. Vanderbilt, who had left the Museum fifty thousand dollars a couple of years before. The Shepard offer was referred by the president to Professor Whitfield, who shook his head:

The substance . . . proves to be a clay—(Silicate of Aluminum) impregnated with Iron (in the coloring matter), Sulphur, and possibly Alum. The material is not fine enough for a paint, the Sulphur (acid) and Alum might easily be removed, but the quantity probably obtainable would probably not be sufficient to warrant an outlay in preparing it for use.

P.S. As a Museum specimen it can only be preserved in a bottle, or can be dried as a block of clay.

HENRY FITCHEW, THE MUSEUM'S JANITOR, TO JESUP, DECEMBER 19, 1887.

I respectfully ask your kind attention to the matter of my salary. . . .

Mr. Fitchew, who was getting sixty dollars a month, was given a five-dollar raise.

EDWARD D. COPE TO JESUP, APRIL 9, 1888.

In accordance with my promise I lay before you the propositions made to you verbally in New York.

I would like to have the position of Curator of Vertebrate Paleontology in the American Museum of Natural History . . . at a salary [of] say $4000 or thereabout. I would be able to increase the collections of this department and make it interesting to the public and important to science.

Cope, then forty-seven, was the famous Philadelphia paleontologist whose bitter rivalry with O. C. Marsh was already a cause célèbre in dinosaur circles. Rich by inheritance, Cope lost most of his fortune through bad investments. His application is marked, "Read before the Board . . . and declined for want of funds," but two years later the Museum paid him thirty-two thousand dollars for some of his fossil mammals, reptiles, amphibians, and fishes, and it subsequently bought from his estate more of the same, for thirty thousand dollars. Most of this money was contributed by Jesup.

ALLEN TO JESUP, APRIL 14, 1888.

The letter . . . here inclosed offers to the Museum, on *deposit*, a series of very finely mounted *heads* of large game animals. I would suggest their acceptance. . . . Mr. [D. G.] Elliot, who has seen them, says they are very fine pieces. He thinks that should they be left here they will never be called for.

Allen and Elliot were voted down by Jesup, who was against *loans*. This policy has not always been followed to the letter. Early in the 1900s, Dr. Lucas issued what an admiring colleague called "his famous regulations for the conduct of modern museums and the duties of the staff." These began: "A Museum is an institution for the preservation and display of objects that are of interest only to their owners. It is also a place where paintings, bric-a-brac, trophies of the chase, etc., may be deposited whenever their owner wishes to have them stored temporarily without expense to himself."

ALLEN TO JESUP, MAY 14, 1888.

I wish to show you a lot of labels in Case D, which have been spoiled by the leak in the roof.

"Should be attended to," Jesup has written on this. Two days later, he received a communication from Professor Whitfield:

Yesterday I understand that persons in the Geological Hall noticed an unpleasant smell at the south end of the room. This a.m., while pointing out to two gentlemen some fossils which they inquired for, they spoke to me about a very bad smell in the southwest corner of the room. On going there I find it almost unendurable. On inquiry from the janitor he tells me it comes from Mr. Richardson's room in the basement where dead animals are stored. . . . Can this be attended to immediately, as the stench is becoming *horrible?*

And on this he wrote, "Mr. Richardson will kindly apply the remedy at once by removal & the application of disinfectants."

The taxidermist's reply was at once forthcoming:

The horrible smell that was so offensive to a few in the Museum . . . came from the dissection of a large Bear and Prussian sheep that came to us in a bad state of decomposition.

. . . Work was at once commenced upon them to make into skeletons. . . . They were all boxed and the offensive parts removed from the Museum.

JOHN D. ROCKEFELLER, SR., TO DARIUS O. MILLS, A MUSEUM TRUSTEE, FEBRUARY 15, 1889.

You were kind enough to call upon me Tuesday, with the information that I had been unanimously elected as a member of the Board of Trustees. . . . I assure you that I very much appreciate the honor, but I am otherwise so burdened with responsibilities [that] I shall not be able to serve, and very reluctantly herewith tender my resignation.

This letter is marked in blue crayon, "This is a great pity & I am sorry. M.K.J." Mr. Rockefeller became a Patron of the Museum, and so did his son, John D. Rockefeller, Jr. He never went on the board either, but in 1922 he gave the institution a million dollars. *His* son, John D. Rockefeller, III, served as a trustee in the 1940s and 1950s, but resigned when he became burdened with the responsibilities of Lincoln Center.

ISAAC H. HALL, CURATOR OF SCULPTURE AT THE METROPOLITAN MUSEUM OF ART, TO JESUP, AUGUST 23, 1889.

There arrived this morning at the Museum, addressed to the curator, a package, which, opened, was found to contain the skull and part of the vertebrae of some sea animal. Supposing that the giver must have intended it for the Museum of Natural History, I herewith transmit it by messenger.

This kind of mix-up has been going on decade after decade. The American Museum has occasionally sent the Met odds and ends of a useful nature. "In behalf of the

Trustees of The Metropolitan Museum of Art, I wish gratefully to acknowledge the receipt of your gift of material which has been of invaluable aid in connection with the work of our Department of Arms and Armor," Mr. Harry W. Kent, the Metropolitan's secretary, wrote Dr. Allen in 1914. Mr. Kent's letter is marked, "Refers to black skins for use in repairs, given from our Museum scrap material.—J.A.A."

THOMAS T. ECKERT, VICE-PRESIDENT AND GENERAL MANAGER OF THE WESTERN UNION TELEGRAPH COMPANY, TO JESUP, SEPTEMBER 30, 1889.

I send by express today . . . the section of an old telegraph pole which you recently saw at my office, and which you thought worthy of a place in the Museum, as illustrating the curious habits of a member of the Woodpecker family.

FREDERICK E. CHURCH, THE PAINTER, TO JESUP, DECEMBER 23, 1890.

Is there a piece of the "Charter Oak" in your magnificent collection of the Woods of our Country? The Charter Oak was a native of Hartford—so was I, and I naturally feel proud of the grand old tree. . . . After its overthrow by a storm I went to Hartford and secured portions of the wood. Among them was a half section of a large branch. . . . It will give me pleasure to send you the piece I described.

COLLIS P. HUNTINGTON, PRESIDENT OF THE SOUTHERN PACIFIC COMPANY, TO JESUP, OCTOBER 9, 1890.

My friends in California inform me that I cannot get any section of the Big Trees that is over 18 feet, as the larger ones are all unsound at the center. . . . Under the circumstances, I shall be able to get only an eighteen foot section.

IDEM, AUGUST 10, 1891.

I note what you say of Mr. S. J. Dill's proposed departure
for California, under Prof. C. S. Sargent's direction, to procure
some specimens of woods for the Museum, and I send herewith
the annual pass good in California over the Southern Pacific
Lines.

Jesup, a Western Union director, was forever on the
lookout for additions to his collection of native woods;
Samuel J. Dill, originally a Museum carpenter, was one
of his chief gathering agents in the field. The president's
banking connections with Huntington, E. H. Harriman,
James J. Hill, George J. Gould, Alexander J. Cassatt,
Henry Villard, and other railroad presidents enabled
him to get free transportation not only for Dill and
his woods but for such Museum bones collectors as Dr.
Matthew, Dr. Wortman, and a host of others. In the
Annual Report for 1906, for example, the Museum ex-
presses its appreciation for "their assistance in granting
our field parties free transportation and in giving our
freight free haul" to the following companies, listed alphabetically:

Atchison, Topeka & Santa Fe Railway.
Chicago, Burlington & Quincy Railway.
Chicago, Milwaukee & St. Paul Railway.
Chicago & Northwestern Railway.
Cunard Steamship Company.
Denver & Rio Grande Railway.
Erie Railroad.
Great Northern Railway.
Missouri Pacific Railway.

Northern Pacific Railway.
Oregon Short Line Railroad.
Southern Pacific Company.
Union Pacific Railroad.
Wabash Railroad.

The Jesup Woods rose to around three thousand, of which five hundred were placed on exhibition in the Museum's Forestry Hall, in a place of honor immediately to the right of the Seventy-seventh Street entrance. In 1921, thirteen years after the death of their sponsor, the Department of Woods and Forestry disappeared from the *Annual Report*'s divisional roster. A couple of decades later, despite the fact that in 1935 Mr. e. e. cummings, the poet, had written Ezra Pound in Europe, "There is a miracle in NYCity. This miracle is worth your travelling to NYCity. This miracle is a 'natural' history museum. . . . I ardently recommend the tree room," the Woods had become an acknowledged incubus. In 1942, a Plan and Scope Committee set up in the Museum recommended that they be destroyed. This suggestion was vetoed, and some twenty years later Dr. Oliver hit upon a more kindly solution to the problem. "The Woods that were on display occupied thirty thousand cubic feet," he has said, "and the rest of the collection took up a lot of storage space. We needed the exhibition area for a modern forestry hall. We offered the Woods to the Smithsonian, which accepted and then changed its mind. So I offered them to the New York Botanical Garden, whose director, Dr. William C. Steere, said he had no room. Then I tried the Yale Forestry School, the University of Michigan, and Syracuse University. All refused. The director of the Antwerp Zoo was here a few years ago, and said he wanted a sequoia, so I gave him one of the Jesups. At the suggestion of Dr. Steere, I got in touch with the Gallery of Woods in Portland, Oregon. It said it would take the Woods if we could get transportation money. [The railroads were no longer in a free-haul mood.] Well, we did, from the Hill Foundation—fifteen thousand dollars —but in the middle of all this the Gallery burned down. They asked us to hold the collection, but we had to send it out anyway. They were able to put it in storage."

The Museum has kept a few of the Jesup Woods in its Hall of North American Forests, a Forestry Hall successor which opened in 1958, and it has retained Mr. Church's Charter Oak branch. Preserved in a glass case, this is now in a storage room.

ABRAM S. HEWITT TO JESUP, JANUARY 16, 1890.

I have received today your circular letter . . . in reference to the raising of $250,000. . . . This application causes me much embarrassment, because I am personally unable to make any subscription to this fund. I am very unwilling, however, to occupy a position in which I cannot do my share with the other trustees. If, therefore, my inability . . . should be regarded . . . as a good reason for retiring from a position in which I cannot do my part, I shall be glad to give way to someone else. . . .

Peter Cooper's son-in-law, an ironmaster who had recently concluded a term as mayor of New York, was an old friend of Jesup's; the Museum's president once gave him two peacocks, which he installed, briefly, on the lawn of his country place, where they made such a terrible racket that he asked his son Edward to shoot them and then had them stuffed and placed on the marble balustrades of the old Peter Cooper house (which his wife had inherited) at Nine Lexington Avenue, just south of Gramercy Park. "Mr. Jesup desires me . . . to say that under no circumstances would he be willing to receive your offered resignation," a Museum officer has written on the back of Mr. Hewitt's letter. "You have been too long the friend of the Museum to be measured by dollars and cents." (As mayor, Hewitt, dealing with dollars and cents in the public domain, had seen to it that the City's annual grant to the Museum was increased.) The Museum's friend stayed on the board, in spite of a feeling he had, at times, that the institution's money-raising techniques were importunate. The year before, enclosing his check for five hundred dollars "in payment of the subscription made by me to meet the expenses of the year 1888," he had written, "A simple notice sent to me by mail that the check was wanted would have received an immediate answer, and I do not understand why it is thought necessary to send a special messenger to follow the subscribers to their homes and offices."

J. P. MORGAN TO JESUP, 1890.

My dear Morris,
   I cannot write. I enclose check $15,000. With this you can pay for the collection. The less said the better to my taste.
                                                    Yours,
                                                    PIERPONT.

This letter was, in fact, written—in longhand, from Morgan's house on Madison Avenue. The check was payment for part of the Tiffany Paris Exposition gems. Morgan, a Museum trustee for nearly forty years, headed a group of the richer board members who underwrote the annual deficit, which often ran to forty or fifty thousand dollars. If he wasn't present at the meeting at which this was brought up, he was given the lead *in absentia.* "Mr. Morgan has pledged ten thousand dollars," Mr. Jesup would say. "I will give ten thousand dollars. Mr. Iselin, will you give five. Mr. Mills? Mr. Pyne?" And he would go around the table until the amount had been subscribed. The checks would come in to the controller during the next few days. Morgan died in 1913, the income tax was born, and everything changed. All in all, Morgan gave the Museum six hundred and fifty thousand dollars.

WILLIAM WALLACE TO JESUP, AUGUST 6, 1890.

The new water closet on the top floor is well under way and I think you will be pleased with the idea of leaving it in its present place. . . . The work in general has gone quietly and well since you were here. In fact, if you had been here all summer, I think you would not censure the architects . . . but a little scolding has done much good.

The building superintendent who scolded J. Cleaveland Cady & Co., then busy with the Romanesque Revival-façaded south wing, was a former Five Points House of Industry boy who had been engaged by the Museum as a clerk in 1880 on Jesup's recommendation. "He has developed into a Christian young man . . . and is now . . . looking for employment that he may have some leisure to study at the Y.M.C.A.," the Home for Homeless Children superintendent had written the founding trustee and future president. Wallace, who had a farm near Albany, was a loyal Museum donor of local fossils and carcasses or skeletons of raccoons, squirrels, opossums, porcupines, pigs, horses, cows, and collie dogs. In 1900, soon after bringing in the remains of a donkey, a dogfish, and a Newfoundland dog, and two coral fossils—*Favosites helderbergiae* Hall and *Zaphrentis gigantae*—he was taxed by Mr. Jesup with taking kickbacks, on a rather gigantic scale, from Museum contractors. He got a big scolding and resigned.

IDEM, NOVEMBER 2, 1890.

The information for the enclosed clipping from today's [New York] Herald was given to a reporter by me some six weeks ago previous to receiving your instructions to *not* give out [any]thing regarding the Museum or its collections and educational work.

The article, which ran to two columns under the headline, "Strange Curiosities in Skin, Bone, Wood and Stone," was on the whole extremely favorable, but it contained a few sentences that may have given the president pause:

That [the Museum's] collections are now on exhibition in a hideously ugly red brick structure, half convent, half prison in appearance . . . is . . . a matter of general information. . . . The . . . departments are . . . in charge of professors, who, as a rule, have a vast amount of technical knowledge joined to a youthful appearance that is startling to a stranger. Professor Starr, for instance, who has charge of the Alaskan collections, has a boyish look and a beardless face, and the professors who conduct the taxidermic department in the basement may have passed the voting age five years, but I doubt it.

ALEX J. BELL, MUSEUM FIREMAN, TO JESUP, DECEMBER 20, 1891.

On the morning of December 1, 1891, I was called upstairs to see Mr. Wallace, Supt. Bldg.—he seemed to be in an excited condition . . . and in a heat of temper discharged me from the Museum's employ for no cause whatever. . . . I trust I shall hear from you and you will settle matters by paying me the $50 due me for the month of December, otherwise I shall commence suit against the Museum.

"I think you better send for Bell & give him $50," Mr. Jesup has written on this letter, which is six pages long. The Museum's housekeeping staff is unionized today; no such complaints come to the president.

POSTMASTER, POST OFFICE, NEW YORK, N.Y., THIRD DIVISION, CITY DELIVERY DEPARTMENT, TO JESUP, MARCH 8, 1892.

I regret that it will not be practicable to comply with your request of the 4th inst. to place a street letter-box inside the entrance of the new wing of your institution. . . .

Problems involving deferred gifts were sometimes brought to presidential attention:

RICHARDSON TO JESUP, OCTOBER 1, 1892.

Going home last evening I sat with Mr. Conklin and in course of conversation he read me a cablegram from London stating that a White Tiger had just arrived and offering it [to the Central Park Menagerie] at $1200. At the time or even during the evening, I did not think much about Conklin and the White Tiger, but today my mind has dwelt upon it a great deal, so that this afternoon I saw Mr. Winser and Mr. Allen about it, and they agree that I should let you know that such a rare specimen is being offered—as it might be possible that the Museum could secure it [and] place it in the Park until its death, when it would be a fixture in the Museum.

"It would be desirable for the Park Commissioner to have the tiger," Jesup wrote on the taxidermist's letter. "Would they not buy it, and agree to let us have its skin when dead?"

HENRY M. FIELD TO JESUP, DECEMBER, 1894.

Rameses the Second was in his day what Alexander the Great was in his—a great king and a great conqueror. When I was introduced to him, he was keeping very quiet, for he was lying in his coffin, in the Museum at Boulak, near Cairo. Here is a piece of the cloth in which he was wrapped as a mummy. It is about *three thousand and four hundred years old!* I give it to you with great pleasure.

Mr. Field was a literary, widely traveled neighbor of Mr. Jesup's in the Berkshires, where the president had a summer home. (He had another one at Bar Harbor.) One of Field's travel books, *From Egypt to Japan*, went into twenty editions.

LOUISA (MRS. JOHN W.) MINTURN TO JESUP, MARCH 11, NO YEAR GIVEN.

You told me at Lenox last October that you thought you could put me in the way of obtaining either the head of a moose or a deer for my billiard room. . . . I am sailing for Europe March 27 and want to know whether you can help me to buy a couple of heads to adorn my walls.

Mrs. Minturn's missive is adorned with the notation, "Moose 50—100. Deer 25. Caribou 50."

JACOB A. CAUTER, SENATE CHAMBER, ALBANY, TO JESUP, JUNE 10, 1895.

The bearer . . . is a personal friend in whom I am deeply interested. . . . I am desirous of getting him a position. . . . He has had over three years' experience as an officer in the penitentiary at Blackwell's Island and has acquired a keen knowledge of the pickpockets during his period of service, and I think would make a most useful man as usher in your department.

JOSEPHINE DIEBITSCH-PEARY, THE WIFE OF ROBERT E. PEARY, THE ARCTIC EXPLORER, TO JESUP, OCTOBER 16, 1895.

I have just had a letter from Mr. Peary in which he tells me you are going to secure him an extension of leave.

Oh, Mr. Jesup, how can I ever thank you for all your goodness to me and mine? Do you realize, I wonder, how much this additional leave means to us? It means a new lease of life.

Peary, a lieutenant in the Civil Engineers Corps of the Navy, had made several expeditions to Greenland. In 1894, when he was stranded there, his wife had appealed to Jesup for help in getting a ship to bring him home, and the president had given her a thousand dollars. Two weeks after her 1895 letter, Peary wrote his benefactor, "I have taken the liberty of attaching your name to one of the Greenland glaciers." Jesup thereupon offered to attach *his* name to the list of candidates for the Century Club, but the explorer declined, on financial grounds. Thanks to the intercession of Jesup and others, he later received further leaves of absence (totaling twelve years), which permitted him to carry on his work in the Far North—and, indeed, to discover the North Pole. These permissions were obtained in the face of a reluctant Navy Department, which apparently didn't *want* its engineer to discover the North Pole; Jesup used pull to help bring them about. "I have seen the Secretary [of the Navy] and arranged the Peary matter," William C. Whitney, a

Museum trustee and former Secretary of the Navy, wrote him in the spring of 1896, after being approached by Jesup. "He [Peary] may get 'waiting orders' so as to disguise it." Six months' leave was granted. It had not been up long when Jesup again sprang into action. "The Museum is already rich in the collections pertaining to Anthropology, including among them the very valuable Arctic Ethnological collections of Civil Engineer Peary," he wrote President McKinley on April 13, 1897, and went on:

> but it is our aim to make this Department second to none in magnitude and completeness. My personal interest is such that I have agreed to personally defray the expense for a series of expeditions, to start this Spring and devote six years to explorations covering the northwestern coasts of North America and the northwestern part of Asia, in the effort to determine conclusively the most important of the unsolved problems in the life history of the race: whether America was originally peopled from Asia, or Asia from America.
>
> Still another very important question . . . is the former migrations of the Arctic races. . . . Peary's researches have thrown light on the question, but the answer is still undetermined. The project for Arctic exploration now proposed by Civil Engineer Robert E. Peary . . . has received the highest scientific endorsement here and abroad . . . and . . . has also the approval of myself and the Trustees of the Museum. . . . I therefore on behalf of myself and colleagues respectfully petition that you will grant Civil Engineer Robert E. Peary, U.S.N., five years leave of absence, with permission to leave the country, and in support of my request add the names of the Trustees of this Museum.

Jesup also petitioned the Assistant Secretary of the Navy, Theodore Roosevelt, who wrote him, on May 17, "Of course I will do everything I can. I will see Secretary

[John D.] Long today about the matter." Eight days later, five and a half years' leave was granted.

During the 1896 waiting period, Peary returned to Greenland, from which, the following year, he brought back "The Ahnighito," or "Tent," the world's biggest and heaviest excavated meteorite (thirty-eight tons and eighty pounds). He had previously imported "The Woman" (six thousand pounds) and "The Dog" (eleven hundred pounds). In an exception to the Jesup no-loans policy, all three were deposited in the Museum, which wanted to buy them, but couldn't afford it. Mrs. Jesup treated the Museum to them soon after her husband's death. Mrs. Peary, acting as *her* husband's agent, had asked sixty thousand dollars for the lot, but settled for forty thousand in the winter of 1909, seven or eight weeks before Peary reached the pole and three years after she had written Jesup:

> . . . The meteorites are all I have and I feel that I should make an effort to turn them into money and invest it so that my children will have something with which they can be educated and fitted to earn their living. . . . Mrs. Jesup would scold me for bothering you but what can I do? . . . I have come to the conclusion that it is much easier to go to the Arctic and do the thing you are interested in and want to do than it is to stay at home, bring up the children, fight your husband's battles and look out for bread and butter for the family. I think hereafter I will do the exploring and let Mr. Peary take care of the home life.

The Ahnighito, which had been hauled up Broadway by a team of thirty horses, was exhibited, with its mates (products of the same meteoric fall), in the Seventy-seventh Street foyer until 1935, when they were relocated in the then new Hayden Planetarium.

Although Jesup didn't live to see the success of Peary's final expedition, he contributed fifty thousand dollars toward the construction of its ship, the *Roosevelt*, through the Peary Arctic Club, a group of Peary backers which he founded in 1899 and of which he was president. The *Roosevelt*'s crew made the Pole on the vessel's second try. On the first, in 1905, Peary, now a commander, set sail with a photograph of Jesup hanging over a Pianola in his cabin; his last stop, before heading north, was at Bar Harbor, where Jesup, summering in his Maine cottage, came aboard to wish one and all Godspeed. On the *Roosevelt*'s second trip, the Pole was reached in April, and news of its attainment was cabled to the world by the commander in September, when he got to Labrador. "The Pole is ours," he telegraphed Dr. Bumpus. "Am bringing large amount material for Museum." President Osborn took care of the reply:

> American Museum profoundly moved. Am delighted with your triumph at last. Mrs. Jesup joins me in congratulations. Your flag and route posted on our polar map this morning.

The Museum's Peary material, which (except for the meteorites) came to it as a *quid pro quo* for Jesup's expedition-backing gifts, included a great haul of musk oxen, caribou, polar bears, walruses, Arctic foxes, hares, and birds, as well as such ethnological items as canoes, sealskin tents, costumes, fishing, hunting, and cooking implements, plus a wooden sledge on which the explorer had reached the Pole and which he had christened the *Morris K. Jesup.* The commander's nomenclatural tributes to the president were not limited to a sledge and a glacier. He named the northernmost headland in Greenland (and anywhere) Cape Morris K. Jesup; the snow camp that sheltered his expedition during its few hours at the Pole was called Camp Morris K. Jesup; and a westerly section of Greenland was named Morris K. Jesup Land. (Alas, it lapsed into synonymy, and is now called Axel Heiberg Land, after the backer of a rival explorer.) Two years after Jesup's death, when the Museum unveiled a statue to him, Peary wrote Osborn, "To Morris K. Jesup, more than to any other one man, is due the fact that the North Pole is today a trophy of this country."

One may not leave the commander without a reference to some *living* ethnological material that he presented, since it gave rise to one of the darkest chapters in the Museum's history. This material consisted of six Eskimos, one of them a boy of six or seven, another a girl of eleven, whom Peary brought back in 1897 from Smith Sound, Greenland, at the suggestion of the Museum's anthropology department, one of whose curators was Dr. Franz Boas. (Peary also brought back several barrels of human bones, which he had retrieved from a graveyard.) After a stay at the Brooklyn Navy Yard, the Eskimos were lodged in the Museum in the care of Mr. Wallace, who had an apartment there. They all developed tuberculosis, and were subsequently boarded either at the Wallace farm, where Mrs. Wallace took charge of them, or in an old house of Mr. Jesup's at High Bridge, New York, where they were placed in the care of a local woman.

During the next eighteen months, four of them died, one
went back to Greenland, and the youngest, Mene, survived here. His father, Kesshoo, was the first fatality.
He died at Bellevue Hospital in the winter of 1898, and
his skeleton, prepared by the College of Physicians &
Surgeons at Columbia, was sent to the Museum. Another
died a few months later and was similarly disposed of.
"One of the Eskimo died on Sunday morning," Mr. Wallace wrote Mr. Jesup on May 16, 1898. "Dr. Boas requested me to have the body sent to New York." The
remaining two died in 1899. "A little Eskimo girl, a native
of northern Alaska, died in Mount Vernon yesterday
[she had been moved to a sanitarium there], and I have
secured her skeleton for the Museum," Dr. Boas wrote
Jesup on June 10, 1899, of the final fatality. "It was
necessary to take action without any delay, and for this
reason I have ventured to make the necessary expenses
without authority. These amount to about $15. I beg to
ask you to approve this expenditure." "Approved as it
has been done," Mr. Jesup wrote on this letter, but the
New York *Sun* did not approve. In an editorial headed
"A Question Under the Burial Law," it quoted a news
item from the *Tribune*—"It is said that the body was
turned over to Columbia College, where it will be preserved and given to the Museum of Natural History,
there being no relatives to claim it" and went on:

> It would be interesting to know by what authority Columbia
> College assumes to take any such course. While it is true that
> our law permits a person to direct the manner in which his
> body shall be disposed of after death, there is no intimation
> that this poor Esquimau child ever gave any such direction.

... There can be no authority to turn the body of this Esquimau girl into a mummy and place it on exhibition in the
Museum of Natural History, unless it be derived from the
girl herself during her lifetime, or from some recent amend-
ment to the burial laws which has escaped our attention.

The surviving Eskimo, Mene, was brought up by the
Wallaces, who got a good deal of newspaper publicity
for their hospitality. In 1907, when Wallace was no longer
in the Museum's employ, this publicity took an anti-Mu-
seum turn that put the *Sun*'s editorial in the shade. "Mene,
the Esquimau boy, longed for but one Christmas gift,
but that one he couldn't have," the *World* started a full-
page article headed "'Give Me My Father's Body!'", and
went on:

He asked back his father's bones that he might put them in
a quiet grave somewhere, where they could rest in peace
forever.

And Mene wept just a little, stoic that he is, when he found
that it couldn't be.

You see, Mene is only a poor Esquimau, without kith or
kin anywhere in all the world. He doesn't own a single thing.
He hasn't a dollar that he can call his own. . . . His tribe (*sic*)
numbers just 234 souls, all told. They live alone (*sic*) on the
shores of Smith Sound. . . . And Mene lives here in New
York, far, far away from them, despairing of ever seeing his
people again. . . . The scientists who were delighted to study
leisurely the [Peary] Esquimaux here in New York have long
since forgotten these simple folk from the bleak Arctic. True,
four of them died here, of tuberculosis, but not until these
wise men had learned everything they care to know.

And then, were not the corpses turned over to the doctors
for the very interesting dissections which added much to our
knowledge (*sic*) on ethnological subjects? But, best of all, the
perfect skeletons were turned over to the American Museum
of Natural History, up in Manhattan Square, where savants

who wish to study Esquimau anatomy may do so quite comfortably.

And that is where the bones of Mene's father, nicely articulated, are now. . . . An upstairs room at the museum is his father's last resting place. His coffin is a showcase, his shroud a plate of glass. . . . Lieut. Peary has long since ceased to concern himself with little Mene. . . . But the boy has one friend at least, William Wallace [who] took the boy home with him. There he lives now, brought up as one of Mr. Wallace's boys, well clothed and well fed and well schooled, perfectly happy, but—

Then he remembers the varnished skeleton with the shiny brass joints up in the museum, and he cries a little.

And so on.

Dr. Bumpus, interviewed at the time, said that the Museum had hundreds of skeletons, and that he was unable to locate Mene's father. The Museum's Eskimo scandal is no longer much of a hot potato today, but Dr. Harry L. Shapiro, head of the Department of Anthropology, is no better at pinpointing Kesshoo and the rest than Dr. Bumpus. "We have lots of Eskimo skeletons," he says. "Plastic surgeons consult them." As for Mene, he became a taxi-driver and disappeared from Central Files many years ago.

On with the Files and the nineteenth-century Morris K. Jesup.

GEORGE HOADLY, A NEW YORK LAWYER WHO HAD ONCE BEEN GOVERNOR OF OHIO, TO JESUP, OCTOBER 16, 1896.

I approve, as every educated man must [Hoadly was a Yale man], of your institution, but before I can consent to become an annual member, I wish to know whether this institution is open on Sunday. If it is, I will at once sign the application. . . . If it is not, I must decline.

The former governor was behind the times. The Museum, originally closed on Sunday, had reversed its policy in 1892, when Jesup, who had once said, "Open the Museum on a Sunday, and it will be impossible to stop there. . . . The end will be the Parisian Sunday," changed his mind, thus causing Mrs. John Auchincloss, a sister-in-law of Early Trustee Hugh, to return her membership notice the following year with a card reading "Mrs. A. declines further membership on account of Sabbath opening." William Adams Brown, the Jesup biographer, has written of his subject's change of mind, "He recognized that a policy which allowed the rich to enjoy pictures and works of art in their own homes on Sunday, while it denied the poor the privilege of similar recreation in the public galleries, to the support of which they contribute by taxation, was an intolerable discrimination."

FRANCIS C. MOORE, PRESIDENT OF THE CONTINENTAL INSURANCE COMPANY, TO JESUP, DECEMBER 15, 1899.

A little lame boy from California . . . eleven years old, has been denied entrance to the Museum . . . with his wheel chair and nurse. . . . I write you in hope that you may grant him a special privilege to enter the Museum.

Jesup got this straightened out (wheel chairs *were* allowed in the Museum; the doorman had thought the nurse was referring to a baby carriage), and scribbled on the back of one of several Moore letters engendered by the episode, "This whole business seems to be the complaint of a much troublesome woman (& there are many such). . . ." It is only fair to point out that Jesup was not a misogynist; "I could not resist the appeal of a sweet woman and I agreed to give her the help she desired," he said of his gift to Mrs. Peary.

MORTIMER L. SCHIFF TO JESUP, FEBRUARY 9, 1900.

I have been requested by the trustees of the Boys' Club . . . to speak to you about the possibility of the Museum . . . giving small exhibitions which it does not require any more, to the Boys' Club.

Mr. Gratacap got up a box of rocks, minerals, and insects for Mr. Schiff, then twenty-two and in his first year of Kuhn, Loeb & Co. partnership. A continuing relationship between the banker's family and the Museum —typical, in a way, of the entente between Central Park West and Wall Street—has flourished for more than eighty years. In 1901, the young philanthropist's veteran philanthropist father, Jacob Schiff, a Life Member since 1883 and an Associate Benefactor at his death, gave the Museum eighteen thousand dollars for an ethnological collecting expedition to China. He was considered for trusteeship around this time, but Mr. Morgan's affections for him were lukewarm, and the matter was not pressed. In 1902, Mortimer Schiff's uncle, James Loeb, a retired banker and founder of the Loeb Classical Library, contributed a goshawk, shot on Upper Saranac Lake. In 1904, Schiff's grandfather, Solomon Loeb, a co-founder of the family banking firm, left the Museum five thousand dollars. In 1912, another uncle, Morris Loeb, a chemist, left the Museum a trust remainder, which, on the death of his widow in 1951, came to over ninety-six thousand dollars—the income to be used "for the illustration of the industrial use of modern products in ancient and modern times."

Mortimer Schiff himself left the Museum twenty thousand dollars when he died in 1931. In January, 1910, his brother-in-law, Felix M. Warburg, had been mentioned in the post-script of a letter from President Osborn to Trustee Percy R. Pyne:

> DEAR PERCY:
>
> Kindly come up and lunch with me. It is *very* important I believe to select [as a trustee] the name of an agreeable Hebrew, because the Zoo, the Metrop.[olitan Museum], the Public Lib. have all done so, and our atti[tude] is becoming conspicuous. [Felix] Warburg has been suggested and there are reasons why I would favor him.

A few days later, the name of an uncle-by-marriage of the Boys' Club Schiff (and of Mr. Warburg) was featured in a letter from Mr. George C. Clark, an Annual Member and a partner in the banking firm of Clark, Dodge & Co., to President Osborn:

> You will remember speaking to me the other night as to a desirable Hebrew to act as Trustee for the American Museum of Natural History. Yesterday, I had a chat with my friend, B. Aymar Sands, regarding Mr. Isaac N. Seligman, whom, you will perhaps remember, I suggested. . . . Mr. Sands agreed with me, in my estimate of the man, that he was public-spirited, very generous, agreeable, and one of our best citizens. I myself have known him for many years, and like him in every way.

Mr. Seligman, whose uncle, Jesse Seligman, had become a Patron in 1884, was bumped by *his* nephew; "After speaking to you," Osborn wrote Clark, "I found that the Trustees had practically united upon Mr. Warburg." The latter was duly elected, became one of the most active trustees, and gave the Museum more than two hundred thousand dollars. In 1933, he was succeeded by his son, Frederick M. Warburg, who, after his father's death in 1937, presented the Museum with the Felix M. Warburg Memorial Hall—some twenty exhibits illustrating the ecology, or environmental interrelationship, of plant and animal life as it exists over forty miles in the Pine Plains area of Dutchess County, ninety miles north of New York. This hall, which includes a red fox, a white-footed mouse in its nest, a monarch butterfly resting on a sumac plant, a woolly-bear caterpillar, and a hibernating chipmunk curled up on top of a pile of about two hundred acorns, was a little slow in getting under way. According to Mr. F. Trubee Davison, Osborn's successor as president, its donor once said at a trustees' meeting, "You know, it's supposed to be a memorial to Father, not to me." The hall finally opened in 1951. "No one was sweeter, simpler, and more modest than Felix Warburg," Mr. Davison said on this occasion. "Primarily interested in making the lives of others better, he established our pension fund in 1913." This fund now stands at more than eleven million dollars.

JESUP TO JOEL A. ALLEN, OCTOBER 12, 1900.

I have been through your Mammal Department this morning, and I must confess that I am not pleased with its appearance. . . . The Walrus Case: The labels are discolored and I noticed some cobwebs around the specimens, and the case is not clean. The Virginia Deer Case: Not at all attractive. The Black-tailed Deer Case: the same as above. The New Foundland Caribou next to the above: not clean; there is a pot, I suppose containing disinfectant, in this case which is not attractive—it looks shiftless. The Moose Case: No labels on

one of the specimens. . . . Mouse and Rat Case: Very poor exhibit for such a nice and expensive case, some of the labels
down—specimens badly placed. Skunk and Badger Collection:
Same criticism as the Mouse. . . . Bear Case: No label on one
specimen, the rocks on which one of the bears are mounted
look dirty. . . . Camel Case: Only typewritten label and
soiled at that; no label on skeleton. Case "U": I think the
specimens are miserably displayed, and badly labelled and
crowded. Case "T": I think this also is too crowded. . . . Two
Giraffe specimens: I think the brass rods should be cleaned
and the specimens brought out for a clearer display. . . . You
will excuse me, Professor, for writing these criticisms. It is my
intention to go through personally all departments of the
Museum, and I have commenced today with yours. I have no
doubt that I shall find in the other departments a good many
things to which I shall be obliged to call the attention of the
Curators.

"Your letter of yesterday duly received, and a few
words in reply seem not out of place," Dr. Allen replied.
"I very much regret that you did not call me down to
go with you through the mammal floor, as probably I
could have explained why certain things you observed
happened to be as you found them." He went on to take
up the president's points seriatim:

I quite agree with you that several of the cases you mention
do not present an attractive appearance. Cases U and T . . .
are too crowded, and have been for several years past, yet
we have to keep crowding in specimens as they are mounted
simply for storage. There is no remedy for this state of things
until there is a chance to expand. . . . In regard to the Giraffe
specimens I did not care to have them mounted until there
was a proper place to put them, but you expressed a strong
wish to have them mounted and we had to put them in what
seemed to be the most secure place. The rods which you

criticize are not brass rods but iron rods gilded, and the gilding quickly turns dark and requires renewal. In respect to the cobwebs in the Walrus case and the can of disinfectant . . . I found they had already been removed when I visited the hall immediately on receipt of your letter. The disinfectant had been placed there to destroy some insects. . . . The specimen in the Moose case does not belong there, being a large African Antelope and one of the recent additions I had not reached in labelling. The Camel in the Walrus case was placed there temporarily for storage and the discolored typewritten label . . . was put there to explain that the specimen was simply placed there for storage. . . . In regard to the Rat and Mouse cases, the case is not adapted for such specimens and they cannot be arranged to look attractive.

And so on.

Jesup was seventy at the time of this interchange; Allen was sixty-two. The president's somewhat conciliatory tone was not uncalled for. In 1885, he had hired the professor away from the Harvard Museum of Comparative Zoology —where, in 1880, William James had written Allen a postcard, "Many thanks for your pinnipeds [*History of North American Pinnipeds*, an 800-page book] which I shall read with much interest. Your working powers are heroic"—to take over, and amplify, the ornithological and mammalogical responsibilities of Dr. Holder, leaving the Florida reef authority free to specialize in marine zoology. The new man had already made his mark as curator of birds in the Agassiz museum, as a collector of "unprecedented ability" (DAB) in the West, and as a monographer of birds and bison, as well as pinnipeds. At the time of the Camel in the Walrus Case, his whiskers were every bit as grand as the president's; he was the founding president of the American Ornithologists' Union and editor of its quarterly, *The Auk;* and he was editor-in-chief of all the Museum's zoological publications. (In the 1887–1890 volume of one of them, the *Bulletin,* he wrote nine of the twenty scientific papers listed in the table of contents.) He was on easy corresponding terms with Marsh, Cope, Baird, Ridgway, Ferdinand V. Hayden (to whose famous Rocky Mountain Survey volumes he contributed a series of articles on Western rodents), William Dean Howells (to whose *Atlantic Monthly* he was also a contributor), and Elliott Coues, an early American historian who was also a prolific bird biographer and a professor of anatomy. The exchange between these men (and others, including the lay public) and Allen, starting in his Cambridge days and running through his thirty-seven years in New York, illuminates not only the curator but the general museum scene. A few examples must suffice.

MARSH TO ALLEN, FEBRUARY 7, 1875.

As an example of the number of Buffalo at present I will add that while hunting on Chalk Creek, Kansas, in Oct. 1872, I got into a herd of at least 50,000. The herd started up the valley before I could get out, and I was obliged to go with them. I had a lively ride of some 8 or 10 miles, and then I stopped behind a small bluff that divided the herd. It was more than two hours before the last of the herd had passed.

Please let me know if there are any particular points on which you especially desire information. . . .

BAIRD TO ALLEN, JUNE 24, 1875.

I am not surprised at your conclusion in regard to the Abert squirrel. Can you pick out a first-rate series of . . . hares and rabbits for mounting and send them to the Smithsonian Institution?

HAYDEN TO ALLEN, AUGUST 7, 1875.

I am hunting all the facts in regard to the Buffalo for you. . . . If you ever come across the fossil fishes I loaned Prof. Agassiz about 6 years ago I wish you would lay them aside for me.

COPE TO ALLEN, MAY 15, 1879.

Yours is received and read with pleasure. . . . I had already received a letter from Prof. Agassiz apologizing in plain terms for making statements reflecting on my honor. . . . There is one man who has circulated still more injurious statements than the ones in question. I hope when he discovers his error he will be as manly as Prof. Agassiz in apologizing.

The man Cope had in mind was Professor O. C. Marsh, who at that time was bitterly competing with the Philadelphian for caches of dinosaur remains in Wyoming. So scandalous were the charges and countercharges of paleontological fraud that the two scientists leveled at each other that their foremost colleague in the vertebrate-fossil arena—Joseph Leidy, professor of anatomy at the University of Pennsylvania and a modest and uncompetitive man—became so disgusted that he abandoned the field of vertebrate paleontology as one not fit for gentlemen and withdrew into *invertebrate* paleontology. Time cures all things, in a way: the office of Dr. Bobb Schaeffer, the Museum's present chairman of Vertebrate Paleontology, contains three photographs of Cope, Marsh, and Leidy happily united in a single frame.

COUES TO ALLEN, DECEMBER 2, 1884.

I am truly sorry to hear what you say in your last letter. . . . I have never thought you sufficiently appreciated, nor paid enough *there* [at the Museum of Comparative Zoology].

. . . You do not say what you expect, or where it is to be. Tell me more about it. I wish you could be here [Coues, a volunteer worker at the Smithsonian, was writing on the letterhead of this Institution, where he was doing some re- search]—is that possible? But it is B.'s [Baird's] settled policy never to have one of his peers or betters in Science about him— so that this establishment is simply a hatching house of hench- men who make an honest living by doing what they are told to do. . . . The active movements in respect of specimens consist largely in taking them in one place and putting them down in another, with special reference to the circus-movements when a show like that in Phila [the Centennial of 1875] Lon- don or N. Orleans furnishes extra funds for extra activity on the part of the queer little pismires who abound in this hill. When Sclater was here, and I took him over the National Mu- seum, I had to hang my head in silence and could only shrug when he asked questions, likening that old curiosity shop to the similar depository of odds and ends they have at South Kensington, where the prototypes of Washington's breeches, and Dr. Mary Walker's clouts, and the wax-figgers generally are exhibited to the unwashed of the British metropolis. . . . When do you think you can begin to codify? I suppose we ought to get [the] thing out before the next meeting. I send back proofs.

Dr. Coues's question was directed, no doubt, to a tax- onomic publication of the American Ornithologists' Union, of which he was, with Allen, a co-founder.

COPE TO ALLEN, MAY 11, 1885, THREE YEARS BEFORE HE WROTE JESUP ASKING HIM FOR A JOB.

Does the Central Park Museum want a Vertebrate Paleon- tologist? and how much will they pay in the way of a salary if they do? If I can get a good salary I will bring my collection along and deposit it if I cannot sell it for what it has cost me, $100,000.

BAIRD TO ALLEN, MARCH 24, 1887.

As you know, we were quite successful in our recent buffalo hunt. . . . We promised each road—the Pennsylvania, the Chicago, Milwaukee and Saint Paul, and the Northern Pacific —giving us passes, the disposal of one of these skins; and the one at the disposal of the Northern Pacific has not yet been called for.

If you want it for the "American Museum," I would suggest that Mr. Jesup apply at once. . . . I believe you have a bull, and if you have no cow, we would prefer to send you that sex. . . . We now value these skins at a thousand dollars each. . . .

ALLEN TO JESUP, MARCH 1, 1889.

The inclosed letter, although sent to me as personal and private, I consider it best to bring to your immediate attention. It has come to me like a thunder-clap from a clear sky, and agitates me very much. The position referred to in the letter is that of an assistant in the Division of Economic Ornithology in the Department of Agriculture at Washington.

It is very kind of Dr. Merriam to consult me about the matter, rather than to seek to get Mr. Chapman away in an underhanded manner.

Of course if I can write Dr. Merriam that Mr. Chapman's salary has been raised to $1200 it will end the affair immediately. For I am sure Mr. Chapman would immensely prefer his present position to the new one now offered, of which he of course as yet knows nothing.

This will also give you some idea of the "market value," so to speak, of Mr. Chapman's services. I should be thoroughly disheartened to lose him. I know of no one who could make his place good.

Dr. C. Hart Merriam was the founder and chief of the Division (later Bureau) of the Biological Survey in the Department of Agriculture and a power in the American Ornithologists' Union. Dr. Frank M. Chapman, an associate curator under Allen, had come to the Museum two years before, at twenty-six, as a volunteer worker, to help Allen assort, catalogue, and arrange birds. His champion's effort to keep him was successful. Chapman became Curator of Birds in 1908 and head of the newly autonomous Ornithology Department in 1920, holding this post until three years before his death in 1945. More concerned with exhibition than with research (unlike Allen), he was a pioneer arranger of habitat groups. According to a 1939 *New Yorker* Profile, published when its subject was seventy-five,

> Dr. Chapman's greatest contribution to museology has been the introduction of the habitat idea in exhibitions. Fifty years ago an American museum's concept of a bird exhibit consisted of a lot of stuffed specimens arranged in a manner reminiscent of the grill of a college club. Around 1900, John L. Cadwalader, an early patron of the [American] Museum, gave Dr. Chapman $1,200 and asked him to get up a bird group with a background that would make sense. Dr. Chapman produced a Cobb's Island, Virginia, group which contained black skimmers and other indigenous birds against a setting of beach composed of actual sand and artificial seaweed, which merged with a painted background of ocean, sky, and birds. Nesting birds were placed on the beach. A good many of the people in the Museum thought this was too informal and that the painted background verged on the sensational, but President Jesup proclaimed it beautiful. . . . The habitat idea has been applied to all the other departments in the Museum and has been taken up by museums all over the world.
>
> In getting material for habitat groups, Dr. Chapman has travelled extensively. . . . [He] has probably spent more time in the society of birds than any other man alive. For over sixty years he has patiently concealed himself in bushes and blinds all over North and South America in order to study at close range the habits of everything from the blue jay and the pelican to the vulture and the dusky-tailed ant tanager.

. . . Dr. Chapman has on several occasions occupied the nests of some of the larger birds himself. Some years ago, marooned by a storm on a small island in a Canadian lake, he moved three pelican eggs from one nest to another and climbed into the vacant nest, which was made of heaped-up sand and pebbles and was well above water level. He sat there in comparative snugness until the downpour was over, feeling exactly like a pelican. Another time, on a beach in the Bahamas, he passed several days in an unoccupied nest in the middle of a settlement of two thousand flamingos, making notes and taking photographs. The flamingos accepted Dr. Chapman as one of themselves and poked about right under his nose. "Seated on the deserted nest," he reported, "I myself seemed to have become a flamingo." . . . [He] has helped build up [the Museum's] collection of bird specimens from about 10,000 to over 750,000 and to make its bird department the best in the world.

Back to the man who championed this splendid ornithologist in his early days and encouraged him for thirty-five years.

RIDGWAY TO ALLEN, MAY 16, 1894.

I have begun the article on *Oreortyx* but hardly know what to write, since you have taken all the wind out of my sails by your review of Ogilvie-Grant's catalogue of the Gallinaceous Birds!

LYMAN G. BLOOMINGDALE, FOUNDER OF THE DEPARTMENT STORE, TO ALLEN, MAY 11, 1897.

I send you herewith a chicken that was hatched at my place in Yonkers about four or five weeks ago. It has 50 per cent more legs than any chicken that I ever saw before, and may be interesting to your Department. I therefore beg leave to present it to the Museum.

The Museum's *Annual Report* for this year does not list this object under its Bird Donations. Mr. Frank J. Gould, a nineteen-year-old son of Jay Gould, had better luck around this time, although in a different branch of zoology. He sent the Museum the body of a St. Bernard dog from his family place at Irvington, and it was voted in. Perhaps because of their family's help in moving dinosaur bones to the Museum free of charge, young Goulds had little trouble in making their institutional presents stick. In 1922, George J. Gould, a grandson of Jay Gould, wrote the Museum from Locust Valley, Long Island:

> While walking through a very thick streach (*sic*) of woods here, I came upon several very old bones which evidently had been washed out of the soil. Weather (*sic*) they are of any historical Value I cannot tell, please inform me weather (*sic*) you want me to send a few bones to you.

"Dear Sir," Dr. Lucas replied:

> I shall be much obliged if you will kindly send us, by express, a few small bones from those noted in your letter. . . . While they may be of no importance, yet on the other hand, they may have come from some Indian burial place and would be of interest.

"The small bones will do as well as larger specimens," he added hopefully.

WINSER TO ALLEN, JUNE 29, 1897.

> I was told today that the hair of the Kangaroo was being destroyed. One of our members left word. Do you think there is anything in the statement?

"I have inspected the Kangaroos," Allen wrote the secretary, "and find nothing the matter of (*sic*) the hair. There is absolutely no sign of recent work by insects."

ALLEN TO THE EDITOR OF THE NEW YORK *Tribune*, FEBRUARY 14, 1900.

In your issue of today I notice a very strange item under the heading, "Would Fine A.M.N.H. Heavily. Game Protection Association to Fight a Bill Regarding Stuffed Birds," which says . . . "A committee . . . will go to Albany today to protest against the progress of a bill introduced a few days ago in the Assembly with such drastic provisions that . . . it . . . will subject the American Museum of Natural History . . . to fines aggregating $100,000 for having in its possession stuffed birds. In the bill's present shape, dead birds, no matter if stuffed for scientific purposes . . . subject the owner to a fine of $25 for each bird. . . ."

Perhaps it would be unkind to say that this note furnishes fresh evidence that all the fools are not dead yet, but the absurdity of the statement certainly warrants strong language. Will you kindly allow me to state the facts in the case? . . . [The bill] does not apply to any person holding a certificate [of] authority to collect birds . . . for scientific purposes . . . [It] . . . clearly provides for the collection and possession of birds for scientific purposes, and . . . makes the American Museum of Natural History an agent under the law for the granting of permits. It would thus seem impossible that any intelligent person could make such an absurd outcry as has been raised in the article here criticized. . . . The whole purpose of the [bill] is to prevent the destruction of song and insectivorous birds for millinery purposes.

The *Tribune* published a correction.

A good part of the Kangaroo inspector's correspondence was devoted to scientific terminology, a subject which has engrossed the Museum's curators for nearly a hundred years. In 1909, answering a letter from Dr. Merriam (the man who had tried, in gentlemanly fashion, to get Chapman away from the Museum), which asked whether, "in the case of the cottontails . . . should not the nomenclature stand *Lepus mallurus floridanus* instead of *Lepus floridanus mallurus,* inasmuch as *mallurus* is simply a new name for *sylvaticus?*" he wrote:

> The whole question is settled by the fact that the rule of priority in nomenclature deals with names and not with things. This is clearly implied by Canons XV and XXV of the A.O.U. Code. If the earliest name applied to any form of a specific group proves to be untenable, the next earliest name for any member of the group takes its place as the tenable name for the group. . . . The only departure from the rule that I recall is where I renamed a species of squirrel described many years before by Wagner under a preoccupied name, and then, by pure inadvertance, proceeded to employ the new name as the proper specific name for the group, which consisted of a considerable number of subspecies. I was promptly "called down" for this lapsus. . . .
>
> You certainly are "muddled" on this particular issue.

Squirrels, on a less scientific plane, were brought to Allen's attention later in the year. "I have been informed that perfectly wild gray squirrels cannot be induced to touch roasted peanuts, such as our semi-domestic park squirrels devour with such relish," Mr. Clinton G. Abbott (who in 1907 had given a members' lecture on "Bird Hunting with a Camera") wrote him. "Would it be possible for you to inform me whether such is really the case in fact?"

"I have never had much opportunity to study wild live

Gray Squirrels, and I know of no one who has had the necessary experience to answer your inquiry," the taxonomist replied.

Allen was not strong on wild wolves, either. "It is reported . . . that wolves never eat the feet of their human victims. Please tell me whether this is true or not," a man from West Virginia wrote the Museum, again in 1909. This query was referred to Allen, who ducked it. "It is so rare an occurrence that man falls a victim to Wolves that I think it would be impossible to answer your question."

The Mammalogy and Ornithology curator's scientific gifts did not preclude an occasional absentmindedness. In 1910, he advised Mr. Outram Bangs, his mammalogical opposite number at the Agassiz museum, "I am sending you by this mail a small Mouse, discovered in our collection, which appears to belong to the Museum of Comparative Zoology, accidentally left from many years ago when I borrowed material for study from the Museum."

Allen was primarily interested in research, and the struggle between this aspect of the Museum and exhibition, which still goes on, is reflected in a 1910 exchange between him and Dr. C. H. Townsend, the Museum's acting director. "I wonder if our rare and valuable sea otter skin should not be mounted. Will you not consider the matter?" Townsend wrote him, and got a thoughtful reply:

I feel reluctant to have unique specimens mounted for exhibition, for the reason that they then become practically valueless for scientific investigation, and quickly deteriorate under the bleaching effect of the strong light they are subjected to in the exhibition cases. In the present case, our skin of the California Sea Otter is the only one extant, so far as I know, and the species is practically extinct if not wholly so.

For these reasons, it seems to me it would be very unwise to sacrifice so valuable a specimen by mounting it for exhibition.

Allen, who in his later years left birds to Dr. Chapman, came to be known as the dean of American mammalogists. He published more than two hundred and seventy papers in this field, some of which exhibited a certain taxonomical severity. In "A Preliminary Study of the South American Opossums of the Genus *Didelphis*," for example, he wrote:

> In his otherwise creditable notice of this group of opossums Temminck makes the singular mistake of reversing the colors of the ears of his *D. azarae*, which he says are yellow at the base with the rest black, whereas just the opposite is true, as noted by Wagner and Hensel.

Temminck's corrector died at eighty-three, almost in harness; a few months before, in failing health, he had been made honorary curator of his department, at full salary. Word of his death was cabled by Dr. Lucas to President Osborn, then in Paris. The French Postal Telegraph office was not up to the Osborn calligraphy in his reply. "DEEPLY MOVED LOSS OF OUR DISTINGUISHED AND BELOVED AVIATOR," the president's cable read. "EXPRESS WARM SYMPATHY TO WIDOW." "I passed the word on to Mrs. Allen, changing the word 'aviator,' however, to 'curator,'" Mr. George H. Sherwood, then the Museum's executive secretary, wrote the director, who was on vacation. "It is a little difficult to think of Doctor Allen as an aviator, although this may be an entirely proper designa-

tion for an eminent ornithologist." The Dictionary of
American Biography says of Allen that he had "above all,
the veneration and love of his colleagues and associates."
This is borne out by a letter dated November 28, 1899,
four weeks before its writer's death:

DEAR ALLEN:
   The friendship of half a lifetime cannot be killed at this
late day, and I am sure you will be sorry to hear that my
disease is desperate. I go into Johns Hopkins Hospital tomorrow, for the very formidable surgical operation which seems
to offer some hope of saving my life.

                                          Yours as ever
                                          COUES

   I seem to have lost Mr. Morris K. Jessup again. During
the last decade of his life, his health, too, was on the
downgrade; the Eskimo scandal cannot have been a tonic,
and his spirits were undermined, around the same time, by
the *Wallace* scandal. "I am not strong in body or mind
just now; this trouble has unnerved me," he wrote, of this
last, to Osborn and Bumpus in 1901, but he moved with
his customary alacrity, on a Museum matter, the following year. Let a *Bulletin* article, "Martinique and St. Vincent: A Preliminary Report upon the Eruptions of 1902,"
by Edmund Otis Hovey (then Associate Curator, and later
Curator, of Geology) tell the tale:

   On May 9, 1902, the civilized world was startled by the news
that a great eruption of Mt. Pelee on the island of Martinique
had taken place the preceding day. On May 10 this news was
confirmed with the addition of details regarding the annihila-
tion of St. Pierre, the largest and most beautiful city in the
Lesser Antilles, and the dispatches also contained the informa-

tion that on Wednesday, May 7, the volcano known as
La Soufriere on St. Vincent had suffered a great eruption attended by much loss of human life and property. Scientific interest in the West Indian volcanoes was of course at once
aroused. . . . Mr. Morris K. Jesup . . . perceived the value of
the opportunity, laid the matter before the trustees . . . immediately, and it was decided to send the author to the islands
as the representative of the Museum. Passage was secured for
me upon the United States cruiser "Dixie," sailing from New
York May 14 with supplies for the impoverished inhabitants of
the devastated islands, and I arrived at Martinique May 21. . . .

Dr. Hovey remained *in situ* for seven weeks, braving
volcanic dust, lakes of boiling water, and avalanches of
rocks and earth while he took notes and photographs. He
made four ascents of Mt. Pelée, where thirty thousand
people had been killed and where steam was still erupting,
and wrote, with scientific detachment, "The freshly fallen
ashes had a curious resemblance to snow, which gave a
peculiar Alpine aspect to the mountain." The "preliminary" report (thirty-nine pages, three maps and charts,
thirty photographs) in which this observation appeared
was never followed up. Its author made another trip to
Martinique and St. Vincent in 1915, with an eye to further
publication, but in 1924, in the course of a long "budget"
letter to Mr. Sherwood, then the Museum's acting director, he wrote:

. . . So much time has elapsed now since the observations were
made that I do not wish to publish without another trip to
Martinique and St. Vincent for the purpose of comparative
and up-to-date observations. I should like, therefore, to make
preparations for another trip to the region, and would ask
that the Heilprin Fund for 1925 be allocated to this end. . . .

Dr. Hovey died, at his desk, while he was writing the thirteenth paragraph of this letter.

President Jesup began to cut down on *his* correspondence around the time he booked Hovey on the *Dixie*, and such messages, addressed to him, as

> . . . I presented to the Museum . . . a pet Rooster of mine that died, with the understanding that it was to be stuffed, put on exhibition in a glass case, with a full description of what it could do and by whom it was trained. . . . I have visited the institution several times to see it but am told a different story every time I make inquiries, at last went to the Superintendent for Information he laughed and said they must be *guying* you. To say the least I think that a very strange remark for a Superintendent of so large and valuable an institution to make. Now I am in a quandry, I think perhaps it is after all only a place to *guy* and have fun with people, they imagine in their greatness to be little fellows. The Bird I valued highly as it was as near human as a dumb fowl could be, it would walk the tight rope, go up and down a ladder, jump through a small hoop one only large enough to let its body pass through, fly through a fire hoop, stand on one leg, fly from the ground to my outstretched arm, and in fact would do almost anything I commanded. . . . He would fight a dog, cat, or man like a South African soldier. . . . If the Museum did not want him and did not intend to do as they agreed, why did they accept him, and in accepting why this delay and *guying?*

were generally turned over to Dr. Bumpus, who had just been made the Museum's first director in a step calculated to relieve the president, who had been *acting* as a director, of some of his responsibilities. "It seems that the rooster was made up into a skin and put away with our study collection," Bumpus wrote the donor of this pet. "This was

due to a misunderstanding on the part of the taxidermist.
. . . The bird has been taken from the study collection,
mounted, and is now practically ready for exhibition."

The president did find strength, however (again, in
1902), to try to interest Andrew Carnegie in his favorite
institution. He received for his pains a typewritten letter:

MY DEAR MR. JESUP,
   One thing I have found out—one Museum is enough, and I
have one on my hands [the Carnegie Museum in Pittsburgh]. I
should be delighted to promise that when I get through with it
I should consider the claims of another; but, between our-
selves, I never expect to get there. I find a Museum a con-
tinual source of interest *and expense.*

Very truly yours,
ANDREW CARNEGIE

with a holograph postscript, *"One Museum to one family.
A.C."*

In 1907, the last full year of Jesup's life, the Museum
had a scientific staff of twenty-five, was visited by more
than half a million people, had over two thousand members, and spent eighty thousand dollars on exploration, research, and publication. Its annual City Maintenance Fund
was $160,000, as against $10,000 in the first year of Jesup's
stewardship; its endowment (about to be doubled by his
death) was just over a million dollars. During the year,
through expeditions which he financed, the Museum's
president gave it five hundred Indian ethnological specimens and twenty-six hundred and sixty-seven butterflies,
bees, wasps, beetles, reptiles, batrachians, and fishes from
Brazil; a collection of tattooed Maori heads from New

Zealand; "a remarkably fine collection of feather-work from Río Negro in South America"; and "three specimens of the very rare *Solenodon paradoxus*," a long-snouted, tropical, insectivorous mammal nearly two feet long. He also treated the Museum to an expedition into the Fayum desert of Northern Egypt, which, under the leadership of Osborn, brought back several hundred fossil remains of ancestors of the elephant and got the Vertebrate Paleontology curator started on *Proboscidea, A Monograph of the Discovery, Evolution, Migration, and Extinction of the Mastodonts and Elephants of the World*, which it took thirty-five years to finish.

Another 1907 Jesup paleontological treat was extramural. On behalf of the Museum, he presented the Senckenberg Society of Natural History, of Frankfurt am Main, with a skeleton, sixty feet long and twelve feet high, of *Diplodocus longus*, a Jurassic dinosaur that had been dug up in 1899 in Wyoming and had come to Central Park West as part of the Cope collections. This sizable gift had been triggered by a 1905 letter from Jacob Schiff, in which the banker, who hailed from Frankfurt, advised The American Museum that the Senckenberg Society's museum would love to have a large American sauropod. The Museum was rich in sauropods (and, as we shall see, every other kind of North American dinosaur), and Jesup came through with Diplodocus, whose unassembled bones were neatly stored in one of the Museum's basement receiving rooms. He paid twenty-five hundred dollars to have the skeleton put together, mounted, transported, and installed in the Senckenberg Museum, which had to tear down a wall to admit it. He was invited to its vernissage, but he did not feel up to traveling, and sent Dr. Bumpus in his stead. (The Senckenberg Society elected Jesup an honorary member, and further reciprocated, soon after, by sending the Museum a skeleton of Mystriosaurus, a Jurassic crocodile from Württemberg.)

The president continued to visit the Museum in 1907, in a wheelchair. That Christmas, following a custom, he arranged for the distribution of new silver dollars to one hundred and sixty-one of its lesser employees. (People on a curatorial and administrative level were denied this largesse.) He died the next month. "During many years of association with him," his successor, Osborn, wrote a condoler, Dr. Endicott Peabody, the headmaster of Groton School, "I learned to admire immensely his idealism and his intense enthusiasm for scientific work. This he displayed, although he did not understand any of the details of science—in fact, it was all a sealed book to him—yet he had intense faith in the results." Two years later, the Museum unveiled the Jesup Memorial Statue in the Seventy-seventh Street foyer, which was renamed Memorial Hall. The statue, carved in Florence, cost sixteen thousand dollars, to which J. P. Morgan subscribed two thousand dollars and Messrs. Schiff and Carnegie a thousand apiece. It showed Jesup in a Prince Albert, sitting on a kind of sheet in a tasseled armchair, holding a scroll on his left knee. A "Commemoration and Presentation Address" was delivered by Mr. Choate, and Mr. Morgan told the sculptor, William Couper, "Mr. Couper, I consider that one of the best statues of its kind I ever saw." President Osborn wrote Mr. Pyne, another statue subscriber, "I consider it an exceptional likeness and work of art."

In the early 1940s, faring worse than the adjacent Plan-and-Scope-Committee-threatened Jesup Woods, the exceptional work of art was reduced to a bust. Trubee Davison, then the Museum's president, was on leave of absence as a colonel (later brigadier general) with the Army Air Forces, and his post was being filled by the late A. Perry Osborn, a trustee, who was a son of Professor Osborn. Mr. Davison, consulted about the statue's transmogrification, has suggested that it was undertaken because the statue was "too big." His theory is borne out by Mr. Wayne Faunce (the Museum man who tried to get E. R. Hewitt to pinpoint the Museum's cornerstone), now in retirement in Vermont, who, in answer to a query, has written:

> The circumstances of the "busting" of Mr. Jesup I . . . recall fairly clearly. . . . The seated figure of Mr. Jesup perched on its high base—all in light marble—occupied a commanding position in front of the Hall of Northwest Coast Indians. Until the New York State Theodore Roosevelt Memorial section of the Museum was erected [in 1936], the Seventy-seventh Street entrance was the Museum's only public entrance.
>
> I joined the Museum staff in 1925. As time went on, it became the consensus that the Jesup statue was "just too much" physically and esthetically in its indoors setting. It seemed unduly massive and overpowering, and became just tolerated rather than admired. It blocked the vista of the North Pacific Hall, and so far dominated the . . . foyer that it overshadowed any temporary exhibits . . . and many such temporary displays were set up, often to stimulate interest in projected new buildings and halls. Before they were moved to the Great Hall of the Roosevelt Memorial main entrance,

the three companion bronze pieces of Carl Akeley's magnificent African Lion Spearing Group were temporarily installed in the Seventy-seventh Street foyer, and there were facetious references, among the staff, to the spectacle presented then of "Mr. Jesup refereeing the Lion Hunt."

According to Dr. Robert Cushman Murphy, Dr. Chapman's successor as head of the Bird Department and now, in his vigorous eighties, Lamont Curator of Birds Emeritus, Mr. Perry Osborn did not see eye to eye with his father and Mr. Morgan about the statue.

The shrinking of Mr. Jesup was, I believe [Dr. Murphy has written], at the instigation of Perry Osborn when he was Acting President, or, at any rate, acting *as* President.

The statue was . . . fully life size, and Mr. Jesup was a tall and imposing man. [This estimate is supported by a July 28, 1885, entry in the office books of the Brewster Carriage Company, in the New York Public Library, which reads, apropos a Jesup order for a "two-horse wagonette on three springs with a standing top," "Make high driving cushion and high under cushion. They are tall people."] I remember him well, in 1906–07, and on one occasion he came in and asked me questions about what I was up to. [Murphy, then nineteen or twenty, was an assistant in the Bird Department, for which he collected skins around Smithtown, Long Island, in whose vicinity he still lives.]

All in white marble, he sat in the Museum foyer. . . . It was superbly Victorian. His collar was starched, his coat a frock, his trousers well pressed. The chair, although white, obviously was plush-cushioned, and around the bottom was a tasselled fringe. With an excess of realism, the sculptor had carved some of these stone tassels slightly awry, or crossed, as though they had been touched by the high shoes of his Marble Eminence. The chair itself was high-backed, and of Italian style—a good job of wood-turning, in stone. On its marble plinth, it brought Mr. Jesup's head up about nine feet from the floor.

> The wrecker, [who] was reduced to tears, was . . . an Italian mason in the employ of the Museum. . . . When I watched him in the process of chiselling Mr. Jesup's head from its underpinnings, he was bewailing the desecration. My personal feelings, however, jibe with Perry's. Although a great man in the history of the Museum, Mr. Jesup's present effigy is big enough!

In any event, the toe of one of the presidential boots has found its way to a desk drawer in the office of Mr. Walter Meister, who came to the Museum in 1916, at fifteen, as a five-dollar-a-week office boy to President Osborn ("I blotted his signature on letters"), and has risen to controller, assistant director, and executive secretary of the Board of Trustees. The effigy itself is now in storage, along with a Julian Story portrait of Jesup, a portrait of President Wolfe, two portraits of Professor Bickmore, and a bust of Dr. Sargent, the director of the Jesup Woods. The Museum has, however, out in the open, three busts and two portraits of Mr. Perry Osborn's father.

4

HENRY FAIRFIELD OSBORN, the fourth and most consequential president of the American Museum, was born in 1857 in Fairfield, Connecticut; reversing a frequent nomenclatural order, he was named after his birthplace. His father, who was born in Salem, Massachusetts, was the president and successful reorganizer of the Illinois Central Railroad. Henry Fairfield, who began to spell out his middle name (in a large, bold signature) as he began to feel really consequential (around 1905), was graduated in 1877 from Princeton, where his thoughts were turned to science by the university's president, James McCosh, a minister and teacher of psychology and the history of philosophy who had espoused the doctrine of evolution before this had gained much acceptance in the cloth; and by Arnold Guyot, a Princeton professor and famous geologist and meteorologist who had helped set up the pioneering weather observation stations of the Smithsonian Institution. The summer after graduating, Osborn and two classmates went to the Rocky Mountains to collect Eocene fossils. "I saw in the Bridger Basin of southwest Wyoming my first fossil titanothere," he has written. Stimulated by this sight, he started to do research for a monograph on the family of this ungulate, which the United States Geological Survey published fifty-one years later under the title, *The Titanotheres of Ancient Wyoming, Dakota, and Nebraska,* in two volumes, weighing thirty pounds. In 1878, he revisited the basin, which Marsh had opened up in 1870, but, unlike Marsh and Cope, Osborn never developed into a field man. He continued his education indoors—in New York, at Bellevue Medical College, where he studied anatomy and histology under Dr. William H. Welch (who later proclaimed Osborn the best pupil he had ever had), and in 1879 in England, where he studied embryology under Francis M. Balfour and comparative anatomy under Thomas H. Huxley.

Although he did not quite live to complete it, Osborn considered his Proboscidea monograph his magnum opus. *This* two-volume treatise was *fifty-three* years in the making, all told, and weighed *forty* pounds. Osborn began to do the research for it in 1889, and he began to put it together in 1907, after his Egyptian expedition. An army of assistants contributed to its period of gestation, and, indeed, finished it up. Volume One appeared in 1936; Volume Two, in 1942. Their chief author kept track of his own activities as enthusiastically as he did those of prehistoric elephants. At the thirtieth reunion of his class at Princeton, he called attention to the fact that he had published two hundred and seventy-six "scientific papers" and seven "scientific memoirs." In his seventies, he issued a book called *Fifty-Two Years of Research, Observation, and Publication, 1877–1929: A Life Adventure in Breadth and Depth*, which listed his memberships in one hundred and fifty-eight "international, national, patriotic, scientific, educational, and conservational societies" and "academies and learned societies." These ranged, in this country, from the National Geographic Society, the American Bison Society, the American Red Cross, the Save the Redwoods League, the Liberal League (co-founder, 1923; resigned, 1924), the Immigration Restriction League (life member), the International Longfellow Society, the Association for the Protection of the Adirondacks, and the Arabian Horse Club of America, to, overseas, the Royal Irish Academy, the Society of the Naturalists of Moscow, and the Cercle Zoologique Congolais, of Terveuren, Belgian Congo. *Fifty-Two Years*, described in its preface as "an 'auto-bibliography,'" contains eight hundred and one titles, arranged chronologically and by subject. A 1930–34 addendum brought the number up to nine hundred and thirty, with two more "in press." (One of these was *Proboscidea*.)

As an autobibliographer, Professor Osborn was elastic. In the roster of his "published writings" he included *co*-written articles (with credit), prefaces to books written by others, class-reunion and other speeches, newspaper interviews and letters to newspapers, earlier Osborn bibliographies (*Fifty-Two Years* catalogues a couple of these predecessors, and No. 830 in the addendum is *Fifty-Two Years* itself), Museum *Annual Reports* (*without* credit to their other contributors) and trustees' minutes, obituaries in the *Princeton Alumni Weekly* and elsewhere, and "A Reply to the Statement of Dec. 18th (1889) of the Committee on the Regulation of Athletic Sports of Harvard University, by the Princeton Advisory Committee and Foot Ball Managers" (privately printed). This appears, in the "Classification by Subject" category, under "Education." Second, third, and foreign editions of Osborn writings are listed separately, and there is also a certain amount of repetition of articles and addresses that were later included, sometimes more than once, in books. The general effect is reminiscent of Bennett Cerf's jokebooks, with old favorites cropping up again and again. *The Titanotheres*, for example, makes sixteen entrances in the "Classified Bibliography," under "Geology," "Palaeontology," and "Biology and New Principles of Evolution," and various subdivisions of these classifications. There are three photographs of the compiler, captioned "The Opening Period of Research," "The Middle Period of Research," and "The Closing Period of Research," as well as pictures, obverse and reverse, of eight medals and decorations conferred upon him. The Osborn likenesses reveal him as an unusually handsome researcher, with a high forehead, piercing eyes, and, in the middle and closing periods, an impressive mustache.

Osborn also kept track of himself in his non-bibliographical works. His byline in *Proboscidea* is followed by a *curriculum vitae:*

> A.B., Princeton, 1877; D.Sc., Princeton, 1880; Honorary LL.D., Trinity, 1901; LL.D., Princeton, 1902; Sc.D., Cambridge, 1904; LL.D., Columbia, 1907; Ph.D., Christiania, 1911; D.Sc., Yale, 1923; D.Sc., Oxford, 1926; D.Sc., New York, 1927; LL.D., Union, 1928; Doctor of the University of Paris, 1931; Doctor of Natural Science, Johann Wolfgang Goethe University, 1934.

Research Professor of Zoology, Columbia University; Honorary Curator-in-Chief of Vertebrate Paleontology, The American Museum of Natural History; Senior Paleontologist, United States Geological Survey; Honorary President, The New York Zoological Society.

This kind of statement appears, in abbreviated form, on the title pages of several of his other books—*Impressions of Great Naturalists: Reminiscences of Darwin, Huxley, Balfour, Cope and Others; Men of the Old Stone Age: Their Environment, Life and Art; The Age of Mammals in Europe, Asia and North America;* and *The Earth Speaks to Bryan,* a riposte to William Jennings Bryan's anti-evolution arguments at the time of the Scopes Trial.

The senior paleontologist was, on occasion, an expensive author. *Proboscidea* cost $280,000 to produce, partly because it contained hundreds of plates but chiefly because its creator had the lordly habit of making extensive corrections, revisions, and additions in proof after proof. It was financed by a fund set up by J. P. Morgan, Sr., whose first wife was an aunt of Professor Osborn. Its dedication read:

IN MEMORIAM

IOANNIS PIERPONT MORGAN

ARTIVM ET SCIENTIARVM

ADIVTORIS ARDENTIS ET LIBERALIS

HOC VOLVMEN

AMICITIAE MNEMOSYNVM

D. D. D.

SCRIPTOR

Scriptor was a dedicated dedicator. *Fifty-Two Years* is formally inscribed "to my wife Lucretia Perry Osborn, enthusiastic supporter of my explorations and researches and ardent believer in my theories"; *Impressions,* "to the memory of the naturalists, explorers, and authors whose creative lives are briefly touched upon here" (followed by a quotation from George Eliot); *Men,* "to my distinguished guides through the Upper Palaeolithic caverns of the Pyrenees, Dordogne, and the Cantabrian mountains of Spain: Emile Cartailhac, Henri Breuil, Hugo Obermaier"; *The Age,* "to my British teachers Thomas Henry Huxley and Francis Maitland Balfour this comparative study of Caenozoic mammals in the Old and New Worlds is dedicated"; and *The Earth* "to John Thomas Scopes, courageous teacher who elected to face squarely the issue that the youth of the state of Tennessee should be freely taught the truths of nature and the fact that these truths are consistent with the highest ideals of religion and conduct. The truth shall make you free." Another Osborn book, *Creative Education in School, College, University, and Museum: Personal Observation and Experience of the Half-Century 1877–1927,* a collection of essays and speeches, is dedicated "to a number of my former students who have devoted their lives to creative work." A list of thirty names, arranged alphabetically, follows.

For a scientist, Osborn had a rather freewheeling literary style. "Admirable as are many of our women teachers, they have neither the natural mastery nor the natural leadership in the education of boys; even in the education of girls, especially in the upper grades, the virile quality is lacking in them," he wrote in *Creative Education* (Number 732 in the autobibliography; the entry's individual contributions are listed under many other numbers), and, again, "It seems a harsh thing to say of the American press, but if I had the power of a Mussolini I would shut it off from our school youth entirely; I would exclude absolutely the irreverent 'funny page'. . . ." And *Impressions of Great Naturalists* (Number 623, and, chapter by chapter, a number of other numbers in *Fifty-Two Years*) contains an offbeat tribute to his uncle and Theodore Roosevelt that may have given pause to some great naturalists:

> The two most powerful men I have known intimately were J. Pierpont Morgan and Theodore Roosevelt. I had the privilege of calling the former "Uncle Pierpont" and have vivid recollections of him as he was in 1867, when I was a boy. . . . Theodore Roosevelt I knew slightly as a boy . . . and in the last two and great decades of his life as my own friend. . . . I never saw a trace of conceit in either Pierpont Morgan or Theodore Roosevelt. The assurance and self-confidence they both displayed in critical and commanding moments were part of the great game of life. Leaders must have broad shoulders, firm necks, and confident and determined faces when the world is full of doubting Thomases, as it always is. . . .

Impressions gives a spirited picture of the author's formative, pre-Museum years. "I had the good fortune to lead my student life between 1873 and 1880 under the spiritual, moral, and intellectual influence of the great men of the Victorian age, the poets Wordsworth and Tennyson, as well as the natural philosophers Wallace, Darwin, Huxley, and Cope," it states in an "Autobiographic Foreword," and goes on, here and there:

Two of my eager Princeton comrades felt the need of anatomy as much as I did, and without the aid of a teacher we started the dissection of a fish, guided by Huxley's "Comparative Anatomy of the Vertebrates." This laborious work on the porgy was followed by an anatomical escapade on the limb of *Homo sapiens,* part of a human cadaver, in one of the unused rooms of the Astronomical Observatory which we converted into a dissecting-room. The venerable astronomer, Professor Stephen Alexander, wondered at the source of the strange odors that filled the observatory, but never discovered the cause! . . . Never shall I forget my first impression of Francis Maitland Balfour as I met him in the great court of Trinity College of Cambridge, in the spring of 1879, to apply for admission to his course in embryology. At the time he was twenty-eight years of age and I was twenty-one. I felt that I was in the presence of a superior being, of a type to which I could never possibly attain. . . . In the autumn of 1879 I moved to London, which was then in the full and glorious tide of Victorian life. Not a member had fallen out of the great ranks. . . . I had the good fortune . . . to come under the commanding personal influence of Huxley. . . .

To Huxley I owe the greatest biological impression that came to me in England, namely, a few words with Charles Darwin in Huxley's laboratory. From the large number of students working there at the time, Huxley singled me out, perhaps because I was the only American, perhaps because of my early palaeontological writing. [Osborn had written, or, to be precise, co-written, a report on his 1877 Eocene excursion, and papers on "The Lower Jaw of Loxolophodon" and "On Some Points in the Early Development of the Common Newt."] I realized that I must make the most of the opportunity, and for a few moments I gazed steadily into Darwin's face and especially into his benevolent blue eyes, which were almost concealed below the overhanging brows, eyes that seemed to have a vision of the entire living world and that gave one the impression of translucent truthfulness.

In the body of *Impressions*, in a chapter on Darwin, Osborn describes this episode more fully:

On December 8, 1879, when Darwin was in his seventieth year and I in my twenty-second, I had the rare privilege of meeting him and looking steadily in his face during a few moments' conversation. It was in Huxley's laboratory, and I was at the time working upon the anatomy of the Crustacea. The entry in my journal is as follows:

"This is a red letter day for me. As I was leaning over my lobster (*Homarus vulgaris*) this morning, cutting away at the brain, I raised my head and looked up to see Huxley and Darwin passing by me. I believe I shall never see two such great naturalists together again. I went on apparently with skill, really hacking my brain away, and cast an occasional glance at the great old gray-haired man. I was startled, so unexpected was it, by Huxley speaking to me and introducing me to Darwin as 'an American who has already done some good paleontological work on the other side of the water.' I gave Darwin's hand a tremendous squeeze (for I shall never shake it again) and said, without intending, in an almost reverential tone, 'I am very glad to meet you.' He stands much taller than Huxley, has a very ruddy face, with benevolent blue eyes and overhanging eyebrows. His beard is quite long and perfectly white and his hair falls partly over a low forehead. His features are not good. My general impression of his face is very pleasant. He smiled broadly, said something about a hope that Marsh with his students would not be hindered in his work, and Huxley, saying 'I must not let you talk too much,' hurried him on into the next room."

I may add, as distinctly recorded in my memory, that the impression of Darwin's bluish-gray eyes, deep-set under the overhanging brows, was that that there were the eyes of a man who could survey all nature.

Darwin's surveyor returned to Princeton to teach, becoming professor of comparative anatomy in 1883. In

1891, he received a joint offer from The American Museum to found a Department of Mammalian Paleontology (later Vertebrate Paleontology), and from Columbia to start a Department of Biology (later Zoology). Anguished cries rose from his fellow Princetonians. "I am in a pitiable condition this morning," Mr. James W. Alexander, of the class of 1860, president of the Equitable Life Assurance Society of the United States and a Princeton trustee, wrote him from the Century Club, and went on:

> Worse than the grippe. There is no strength in me. I have just read in the *Tribune* that you were deliberating over a call from Columbia. I had heard a rumor, but I didn't believe that President [Seth] Low had the nerve to stretch out his hand towards a Princetonian of the Princetonians in our very faculty. If you succumb, I shall feel like giving up my enthusiasm in our struggle to make Princeton a great university. . . . I assure you that there are hundreds of us—and those the men who are enlisted heart and soul to urge Princeton on—who will hold our breath until we hear what your determination is. You are one of the most thoroughly appreciated men in the faculty. We cannot replace you. You will deal a deadly blow at our prestige and progress if you leave us. . . . All I can say is that I know I speak for the Trustees and the Alumni, when I beg you on my knees to stand by us, and assure you that you have the respect, confidence, affection, and fealty of us all.

Mr. Alexander's genuflection was in vain. Three months later, Mr. Wallace, the Museum's building superintendent, wrote President Jesup, who was summering at Bar Harbor, "Professor Osborn has been here twice since you left the city, and has been looking at his room. He seemed very much pleased with it." Uncle Pierpont's nephew, now married to a general's daughter and the father of several children, brought to the Museum staff a panache that seems to have escaped the frame of reference of the Swiss consul in New York. "In conformity with instructions received from my Government, I have the honor to request your kind information with reference to Professor Osborn of your Institute," this official wrote Mr. Jesup shortly after the Professor had settled down in his new room. "As a daughter of a very respectable family has been engaged as governess . . . the Department of the Exterior at Bern wishes to obtain certainty as to the respectability & moral reputation of the family in which she is to enter in the Capacity of governess."

The Columbia-American Museum picture, and Osborn's seminal role in it, have been well described by Dr. Edwin H. Colbert, former chairman of the Museum's Department of Vertebrate Paleontology, in *Curator*, a Museum quarterly, in an essay called "The University in the Museum":

> The history of the university museum of natural history in North America had its beginnings with Louis Agassiz, the founder of The Museum of Comparative Zoology at Harvard College. . . . The example was followed. . . . Thus there arose and developed such outstanding museums as the Yale Peabody Museum, the Museums of the University of Michigan and the Museum of Vertebrate Zoology and Museum of Paleontology at the University of California at Berkeley. . . . Let us now turn to the City of New York, to observe a different pattern of museum and university relationship, a pattern that has involved, not the growth of a museum within a university, but conversely the entrance of a university *into* a museum. The story as it will be told here involves The American Museum of Natural History and Columbia University.

The story begins in 1891, when Henry Fairfield Osborn
. . . was invited to New York . . . and began his new tasks
with gusto.

The American Museum was entering a period of remarkable growth, and Columbia University was in the throes of
transforming itself from a small men's college to a great
university. . . . Osborn rose to the opportunities. . . . He
established the Department of Biology at Columbia . . . and
he began the formidable task of building a collection of fossil
vertebrates at the Museum, where hitherto there had been
virtually no such collection.

. . . There was a large and excellent collection of fossil
fishes at Columbia, housed in the School of Mines. This
collection had been made by Prof. John Strong Newberry,
the first Professor of Geology at Columbia. . . . Newberry
. . . trained Bashford Dean . . . who became . . . Professor
of Zoology at Columbia, Curator of Fossil Fishes at The
American Museum, and, in his later years, Curator of Armor
at the Metropolitan Museum. . . .

It is undoubtedly fortunate that Osborn came to New York
on a dual appointment. He made the most of it. Instead of
dividing his loyalties and schedules, he coordinated his efforts
with those of his associates to establish an integrated program
of teaching at Columbia and of collecting and research at the
Museum. . . . Two of Osborn's students assumed and developed . . . the programs that were to prove so fruitful to
both institutions. One of these men was William Diller Matthew [Dr. Colbert's father-in-law], a towering figure in the
history of North American vertebrate paleontology, who
played a major role in building up and studying collections
at the Museum. The other was William King Gregory, who
at an early stage took over the teaching at Columbia (in
1909, after Osborn, now President of the Museum, had given
up his university courses) and who, through a long career
as an incomparable authority on all of the vertebrates, fossil
and recent, trained an extraordinary phalanx of vertebrate
paleontologists, zoologists, and anatomists. . . .

Even before the consolidation of teaching under . . . Professor Gregory, there had been a physical move from the

University . . . to the Museum. . . . All graduate instruction in vertebrate paleontology became centered at the Museum, where the fossils were housed. . . . The Newberry Collection of fossil fishes was transferred to the Museum . . . which . . . in turn, [furnished] space and facilities for Columbia students of fossil vertebrates. Thus the University entered the Museum.

. . . For many years a comfortably large and well-equipped seminar room at the Museum has been reserved exclusively for the instruction of Columbia students. . . . Doctoral candidates frequently participate in Museum expeditions. . . . This arrangement . . . has produced an array of vertebrate paleontologists and anatomists that has made the Museum-Columbia rooms and laboratories a world center of paleontological-anatomical scholarship.

The generator of this scholarship was also a great man for display. He suspected that large fossils were conducive to a large attendance, so in the Museum's exhibition halls he subordinated fossil fishes and birds to dinosaurs, mastodons, and other impressively sized reptiles and mammals. Although, except for occasional lightning visits, he made no Western field trips himself, he kept the place well supplied with skeletons by sending his staff paleontologists out to Wyoming, Kansas, and Nebraska. The chief pioneers among these were Jacob Wortman, W. D. Matthew, Walter Granger, and Barnum Brown. The last two collected and studied bones for the Museum for a total of one hundred and seventeen years. Granger joined up as an assistant taxidermist in 1890, when he was seventeen, and was Curator of Fossil Mammals when he died in 1941. Brown was twenty-three when he came to Seventy-seventh Street in 1897, fresh from the University of Kansas. He retired as Curator of Fossil Reptiles in 1942, when he was sixty-eight, but remained active emeritus, continuing to excavate skeletons and write papers about them until he died, a few days before his ninetieth birthday. He helped start the Museum's dinosaur collection, which is unrivaled, and went on to dig up more dinosaurs than any man who ever lived. He had no sooner arrived at the Museum than Osborn dispatched him, as a Granger assistant, to Como Bluff, Wyoming, where the Museum's first two dinosaurs were unearthed. He was interviewed for *The New Yorker*'s Talk of the Town Department sixty-six years later:

> Dr. Barnum Brown . . . was looking forward to a Museum party in honor of his ninetieth birthday, to be celebrated next Tuesday, when we called on him at his two old rolltop desks *in situ* the other afternoon. He was rosy and clean-shaven, his blue eyes were twinkling, and he was wearing a dark-blue suit and a blue-and-white bow tie with dark- and light-blue polka dots. He explained that he had two desks because of the pressure of work. "I retired as curator of fossil reptiles twenty-one years ago," he said, "but I'm busy with my memoirs, and as consultant to the Sinclair Oil Corporation I'm supervising the preparation of an exhibit of dinosaurs that this company is getting up for the World's Fair next year. Life-size replicas of nine dinosaurs in Fiberglas—durable in all temperatures—are being put together at the Louis Paul Jonas Studios, at Hudson, New York. I go up there every week or so to check on progress and give advice. . . ."
>
> Dr. Brown . . . began to collect dinosaurs and other prehistoric animals for the Museum in 1897. . . . He secured its first reptile skeleton, Diplodocus; later on, among his plethora of finds, he excavated *Tyrannosaurus rex*, the largest of the carnivorous dinosaurs; *Colossochelys atlas*, the largest known land tortoise; and a skull of Probosuchus, the largest known crocodile.
>
> . . . "I remember one morning in the winter of 1899," he

said, "when Professor Osborn called me into his office at nine o'clock and said, "Brown, the Princeton Museum's Patagonian expedition is leaving at eleven o'clock this morning. I want you to go along to represent the American Museum." I was twenty-six and unmarried. I said I'd go if he'd have the necessary equipment on the ship. This included a mattress from John Wanamaker. Well, it arrived, but it was a double-bed mattress. You couldn't put it on a pack horse."

We asked how long the expedition lasted.

"One year," he said, "but I stayed away for another year. I got some interesting fossils on the Patagonian coast—I used a prospecting pick, a crooked awl, and a whisk broom—and then I decided to circumnavigate Tierra del Fuego, to see what was going on there, paleontologically speaking. I hired a six-ton cutter, but it capsized in a storm, and I floated to shore on a broken hatch cover. I didn't know how to swim. Would you like to hear about the time I fell down a volcano?"

Such a question deserves only one reply.

"Luckily, it was an extinct volcano," Dr. Brown said. "In 1933, when I was sixty, word came to us at the Museum that the mummified remains of an extinct sloth had been found in a crater in New Mexico, north of El Paso. A Yale man bought it for the Peabody Museum before I could make an offer for my department, so I went down there and went down the crater on two ropes. I thought there might be another sloth. The hole was about eight feet by four, possibly six, and you backed down into it like a bear. I was wearing high exploring boots with hard soles, and I slipped about ten feet. The outsides of my hands got skinned on the volcanic rock, and the insides were burned by the ropes. I yelled, and two boys who were with me—just above me—got me on a ledge, took off my boots, and tied a rope around my waist, and I managed to climb up. I never did get an extinct sloth, but I did get some first-class Pleistocene fauna out of that hole—rattlesnakes, rock squirrels, and coyotes, all mummified.

"It's easier to tell you where I *haven't* been," Dr. B. continued, when we asked him to sum up his geographical wanderings. "The only major land areas I haven't worked are

Australia, New Zealand, Madagascar, and the South Sea Islands. The rest of the world has been my hunting ground, from the Arctic to the Antarctic." His most recent hunt, in 1956, took him to Montana, where he dug up a skeleton of Plesiosaurus, a Mesozoic marine reptile. He invited us to cross the hall to the vertebrate-paleontology laboratory, where this was being mounted, and urged us to join him in some coffee.

"Once I've finished the Sinclair job," he said, pouring a couple of cups from a steaming pot on a grill at one end of the room, "I hope to go to the Isle of Wight and pry some dinosaurs and other fossils out of its eight-hundred-foot cliffs. I propose to go around that island in a helicopter with a six-power glass—the highest power you can use on anything that vibrates; with it, you can see the barb on a barbed-wire fence a quarter of a mile away—and pinpoint the places on the cliffs where the most promising bones are. Then I'll come over the top in a painter's rig, cover those spots with shellac, and cut them out. My wife says I'm too old for this sort of thing, but I don't believe a word of it. I have all my teeth left but two. I had a bad toothache in Guatemala a few years ago—I was picking up some ocellated-turkey skins for our Bird Department there—and a local dentist wanted to pull some of my teeth out, but I said, "No, you don't. I'm shooting for a hundred, and I've got to have them.""

Alas, Dr. Brown's shot went wide. He died three days after his interview, which was never published. During his —and his colleagues'—early digging days in the Rockies, carload after carload of Western reptiles, ungulates, and other fossil mammals came in to Central Park West, transportation free, on the roadbeds of the Erie, Missouri Pacific, and other indulgent railroads. The first Brontosaurus, one of the largest herbivorous dinosaurs known— or, at any rate, *half* of one—rolled in in 1899 from an excavation near Como Bluff that came to be known as

1. Albert S. Bickmore, the man who dreamed up and named The American Museum of Natural History, is depicted here during a tense moment on a volcano in Lontar, one of the Spice Islands. "Saved by Grasping a Fern," the caption on this frontispiece to his 1868 book, *Travels in the East Indian Archipelago*, reads. "The stones on which my feet were placed gave way," he wrote. "This threw my whole weight on my hands, and at once the rocks, which I was holding with the clinched grasp of death, also gave way, and I began to slide downward. My only hope was to seize *that fern*." He seized it and lived to see his dream come true.

2. This is the way Professor Bickmore looked in 1902, forty years after the Fern, when he was Curator Emeritus of the Department of Public Instruction, which organized illustrated lectures on natural history for the school children of New York City and State. Greatly amplified, it is perpetuated today in the Department of Education.

3. Morris K. Jesup, a retired banker, was a Museum incorporator and its devoted, full-time president from 1881 until his death in 1908. He and his wife gave it over six million dollars. He was rewarded posthumously by this marble statue, which occupied a commanding post in the Seventy-seventh Street foyer until the early 1940s, when it was reduced to a bust. A toe of one of the presidential boots survives, in a desk drawer of the controller.

4. Admiral Robert E. Peary, the discoverer of the North Pole, was greatly aided financially by President Morris K. Jesup. Peary reciprocated by shipping to the Museum a vast quantity of Arctic animals and artifacts, including a wooden sledge on which he reached the Pole and which he christened the Morris K. Jesup. He also named a glacier, a promontory, and a westerly section of Greenland after Jesup, but these remained *in situ*. Peary's most imposing monument at the Museum is "The Ahnighito," or "Tent," the world's biggest and heaviest excavated meteorite, now in the Hayden Planetarium. It took a team of thirty horses to haul it up Broadway.

5. Louis P. Gratacap, a gentleman of the old school, began to sort out mineralogical specimens for the Museum in 1876, when he was in his twenties. He became a curator of minerals, geology, and shells. In his spare time, he wrote twenty or thirty books, some of them novels and science fiction, whose *mises en scène* ranged from Newport to Mars. He died in 1917 and was buried in a family vault in Trinity Church.

6. Dr. Joel A. Allen (left) was Curator of Birds and Mammals from 1885 until his death at eighty-three in 1921. The founding president of the American Ornithologists' Union, he was editor-in-chief of all the Museum's zoological publications. "Many thanks for your [monograph on] pinnipeds which I shall read with much interest. Your working powers are heroic," William James, the philosopher, once wrote him on a postcard.

7. The elder J. P. Morgan (right) became an American Museum incorporator at thirty-one and was the most influential trustee for several decades. He helped finance a number of expeditions, but he was more interested in art than in natural history, and his greatest gifts were those of gems and precious stones. His total Museum benefactions came to six hundred and fifty thousand dollars.

8. Henry Fairfield Osborn, the well-connected son of a railroad president, was the outstanding architect of the American Museum's growth and fame. The Museum was his life. His association with it lasted for forty-five years, and he was its president for twenty-five. During his tenure, thanks largely to his useful friendships and aggressive leadership, its building space more than doubled, its scientific staff and annual New York City appropriation trebled, its membership quadrupled, and its endowment funds septupled. Professor Osborn was, moreover, a renowned vertebrate paleontologist, indefatigable in collecting, showmanship, original research, and publication. Early on, he turned down the secretaryship of the Smithsonian Institution to devote his protean talents to Central Park West. When he died, at seventy-eight, his department's exhibits of fossil vertebrates, dominated by the famous dinosaurs, were second to none in the world.

9. Dr. Frank M. Chapman, who busied himself with birds at the Museum for fifty-eight years and was Curator of Ornithology for more than three decades, was the father of the habitat type of exhibition. He did more to popularize birds than anyone since Audubon. He liked the way they looked and the way they sang, and in the field he often pretended to be a bird himself, to gain their confidence. He is shown here at Barro Colorado Island, in Gatun Lake, in the Panama Canal Zone, where he spent many a happy birdy winter.

10. Theodore Roosevelt, shown here with the fruit of one of his African hunting trips, gave many specimens of wildlife to the Museum. The Roosevelt Memorial Building, fronted by his equestrian statue, was named after him. His father, after whom *he* was named, was a Museum incorporator and charter trustee.

11. Carl E. Akeley, explorer, hunter, taxidermist, and animal sculptor, made three African expeditions for the Museum and brought back and prepared many of the specimens in the Akeley African Hall. His group of African elephants has been called the greatest feat in modern taxidermy. He is shown here with a leopard that he killed bare-handed. Weakened by a bout with an elephant, he died in 1926 in the Belgian Congo.

12. James L. (Jimmy) Clark, one of the Museum's great field collectors and preparators, supervised the mounting of the habitat groups for the Akeley African Hall, the Vernay-Faunthorpe Hall of South Asiatic Mammals, and the North American Hall of Mammals. He is shown here working on a model for a swamp deer group in 1926, when he was forty-two. He was twice that age and, as Director Emeritus of Preparation and Installation, an occasional Museum visitor when this caption went to press.

13. Dr. Leonard C. Sanford (left), one of the Museum's most active trustees in the 1920s and 1930s, persuaded Mrs. Harry Payne Whitney to treat it to the famous Rothschild collection of two hundred and eighty thousand bird skins, thus making the Museum peerless in birds. He was also an ornithological angel *in propria persona*, especially in New Guinea, where a new Papuan golden-crowned bowerbird, secured by a Museum scientist, was named in his honor.

14. Roy Chapman Andrews (right), the Museum's most celebrated staff explorer, mounted and conducted some grand expeditions into Mongolia in the 1920s that discovered rich fossil fields and yielded such novelties as parts of a Baluchitherium, a tree-browsing rhinoceros, and twenty-five dinosaur eggs, which gave the Museum invaluable publicity. Dr. Andrews was director of the Museum from 1935 to 1942.

15. Felix M. Warburg was a Museum trustee for twenty-three years. He gave it more than two hundred thousand dollars, and in 1913 he set up its Pension Fund, which now stands at nearly ten million dollars. The Warburg Memorial Hall, dedicated largely to ecology, was given in his honor by his successor-trustee son, Frederick M. Warburg. "No one was sweeter, simpler, and more modest than Felix Warburg," President Trubee Davison said at its opening.

16. F. Trubee Davison, president of the Museum from 1933 to 1951, successfully piloted the institution through the Depression. The son of a Morgan partner who had been a Museum trustee, he set up fund-raising committees "to get small contributions, because the big ones weren't there." He and his wife went to Africa in the 1930s and shot four of the elephants in Akeley Hall. A World War I aviator and an old friend of Charles A. Lindbergh, Mr. Davison once got a Lindbergh plane and hung it in the Museum, but it was presently removed on the grounds that its connection with natural history was problematical.

17. Dr. Albert E. Parr, an ichthyologist and a writer on museum architecture, was director of the American Museum from 1942 to 1959. He was an exponent of colorful exhibition techniques, and he put staff salaries on a more equable basis. He now lives in New Haven, where he was formerly professor of oceanography at Yale and director of the Peabody Museum, but he occasionally drops in at the American Museum of which he is Director Emeritus.

18. Alexander M. White, president of the Museum from 1951 to 1968, is shown here admiring a citation presented to him on the occasion of his tenth anniversary in office. The man at the left is Dr. James A. Oliver, who became director in 1959. Dr. Oliver is a reformed herpetologist; Mr. White is an investment banker.

Bone Cabin Quarry, for reasons made clear in one of Dr. Colbert's books, *Dinosaurs: Their Discovery and Their World:*

> In 1897 [Osborn] sent Walter Granger . . . to Como Bluff. . . . Granger found that the old Marsh quarries were pretty poor picking—they had been cleaned out. He therefore scoured the countryside several miles to the north of Como Bluff, and one fine day he found what he wanted. In the middle of an open plain was a small, solid cabin, built by a sheepherder as his own domicile. Granger found to his amazement that the cabin was built out of huge dinosaur bones! And all over the ground around the cabin were more bones, weathering out of the rocks in which they had been entombed for so many millions of years.
>
> Here was the place to dig. . . . Once more, as in the palmy days of Marsh . . . great quantities of bones were taken from the ground, this time to be shipped to New York instead of New Haven. Professor Osborn got the dinosaurs he wanted to exhibit . . . and today [1961] the great skeleton of Brontosaurus from Bone Cabin Quarry dominates the hall in which it is displayed, as popular a museum piece as it was fifty years ago.

It took several years to get Brontosaurus into shape. The missing parts of the skeleton were modeled with the help of Marsh's old museum, the Peabody at Yale, and in 1905 the distinguished sauropod, nearly seventy feet long and over fifteen feet high, was installed in the center of a new Hall of Fossil Reptiles.

In readying displays for this hall, Osborn employed methods that were not at first universally appreciated in paleontological circles, where—in the 1890s—the prevailing idea was that bones were no business of the general public, but should be left inarticulated in museum drawers or on shelves for the exclusive benefit of scientists. Dr. George Brown Goode, the director of the National Museum in Washington, on being advised in 1896 by Dr. Charles Schuchert, then an honorary aid in this museum's Department of Paleozoic Fossils and later Marsh's successor at Yale, of the merits of an American Museum brontothere restoration, replied, "Mr. Schuchert, I admire your enthusiasm, but what you have seen is not Fine Paleontology, but Fine Art." The Smithsonian eventually mended its ways. "Reformation [of fossil-vertebrate exhibitions] began with Henry F. Osborn," Dr. Schuchert himself wrote in 1940. "Following his example, there began to appear in one museum after another articulated fossil skeletons standing in lifelike poses, which fascinated the interested visitor, and which were great educators not only for the general public but even more for the paleontologist."

In bringing about this reformation, which he extended to non-fossils as well, Professor Osborn drew upon the talents of several Fine Art practitioners. One of them, Charles R. Knight, was a freelance painter and sculptor who began to make drawings, murals, and fossil models of animals and prehistoric men for The American Museum in the early 1900s. The essay on paleontology in the famous Eleventh (1911) Edition of the Encyclopaedia Britannica, which was written by Osborn and illustrated almost exclusively with American Museum material, has seven Knight pictures of ichthyosaurs, dinosaurs, and Upper Miocene horses, all of them captioned as having been drawn "under the direction of Professor Osborn." A particularly lively one shows Allosaurus, a carnivorous Upper

Jurassic dinosaur, munching away at the carcass of Brontosaurus Marsh, its herbivorous contemporary, while a friend
(another Allosaurus) looks on, enviously. Professor Osborn was later bumped from the Encyclopaedia as a
writer (although he is now *in* as a subject, with the tem-
perate comment, "His books combine literary art and scientific information"), but the article on paleontology in
this compendium's latest edition is *entirely* illustrated with
twelve Knight pictures of mammals and reptiles—all now
taken, however, from his work for the Chicago Natural
History Museum, with no reference to their "direction."
Osborn's instructions to the artist have sometimes been
superseded by later knowledge. "It was because of this
[three-fingered, sharp-clawed] structure of the hand that
Ornitholestes [a small Jurassic coelurosaur] was given its
name, which means 'bird catcher,' by Osborn," Dr. Colbert writes in *Dinosaurs*. "He envisioned this dinosaur as
leaping up and catching primitive birds with its hands,
and it was restored in such an attitude by the great por-
trayer of prehistoric animals, Charles Knight. Very probably *Ornitholestes* was not spry enough for this; it more
likely pursued small reptiles, such as lizards, and other
small ground-living animals." Osborn himself manfully
corrected his error in a 1916 paper published in the Museum *Bulletin:*

> The new subgeneric or generic name *Struthiomimus* is pro-
> posed for the Belly River (Fort Pierre) stage of the Orni-
> thomimidae.
> The discovery of the skull of the Belly River "*Ornithomi-
> mus*" occasioned one of the greatest surprises in the whole
> history of vertebrate paleontology because it proved that both

in head and limb structure this animal was non-raptorial. *Struthiomimus* (*Ornithomimus*) has no adaptations in its limbs nor in its jaws for seizing an active prey; on the contrary, the extremely small head and slender jaws entirely without teeth most nearly resemble those of the ostrich (*Struthio*). Nor is the recently discovered fore limb analogous to that of any of the carnivorous dinosaurs. . . . These surprising discoveries necessitate a reconsideration of the structure and habits of *Ornitholestes*, which at the time of its first description by Osborn derived its name from its supposed bird catching propensities (*Ornithos*, ὄρνις, bird, lestes, λῃστήσ, robber) [*lestes* λῃστής (sic)]. *Ornitholestes* . . . is doubtless related as a family to *Struthiomimus* (*Ornithomimus*). . . . In the light of our fuller knowledge of the *Struthiomimus* (*Ornithomimus*) skeleton a restudy of *Ornitholestes* indicates that it also has partially lost its raptorial characters; the teeth are small and feeble, in the manus the two central digits . . . are closely appressed and not adapted to seizing or holding a struggling live prey, as Osborn imagined in restoring this animal as seizing *Archaeopteryx;* the manus is relatively feeble. . . . In brief, *Ornitholestes* is a small, subcarnivorous dinosaur of the cursorial, bipedal type. . . . The original reconstruction of [its] skeleton . . . is very inaccurate. . . .

This paper seems to have escaped the attention of Dr. Frederic A. Lucas, who, in 1927, when he was honorary director of the Museum and a member of its Committee on Popular Publications, turned out a popular publication, or guide leaflet, called "The Dinosaur Halls" in which he listed Ornitholestes as "bird robber. Alluding to the theory that his activity enabled him to catch birds." This listing persisted in the fifth edition of this leaflet in 1939. For that matter, the original Osborn-Knight version of Ornitholestes, a 1903 sketch depicting it with Archaeopteryx (the oldest fossil bird) in its manus, is still on display, in the Hall of Early Mammals.

Another Fine Art practitioner, and one, unlike Knight, concerned with contemporary animals, was Carl E. Akeley, a taxidermist, sculptor, explorer, hunter, photographer, and inventor whose name is perpetuated at the Museum in the Akeley Memorial Hall of African Mammals. This eye-filling sequence of twenty-eight habitat groups, arranged around a central non-habitat group of eight mounted elephants, originated with Akeley. What with its incredibly detailed backgrounds of artificial leaves, blades of grass, rocks, flowers, and so on, the hall cost around a million dollars to install. It opened in 1936, ten years after Akeley's death and forty years after he made his first trip to Africa. Akeley is undoubtedly the only job applicant whom the Museum turned down and subsequently named a hall for. Born in upper New York State in 1864, he went to work for Ward's Natural Science Establishment at nineteen, and, after three years there, besought Professor Allen for a taxidermic post. "Believe I can give you satisfaction in all classes of taxidermy and also on mounting small skeletons," he wrote. Nothing came of this, and he presently took his stuffing and mounting talents to the Milwaukee Public Museum, where he spent eight years. In 1896, he moved over to the Chicago Natural History Museum (then the Field Columbian Museum), where he became chief of the Department of Taxidermy and where he perfected a new, lifelike technique of mounting animals that involved modeling in clay and spraying with shellac. Such was its success that in 1909 The American Museum came to its senses and recruited him to its staff. Akeley's life was a dream of Africa. In his first year at Chicago, Daniel G. Elliot, the Chicago museum's curator of zoology and the early birdy friend of the New York museum, took him to that continent to get zoological specimens. He went on one more African expedition for Chicago, and on three much more ambitious ones for New York, observing, shooting, photographing, and bringing back for cosmetic treatment gorillas, lions, elephants, leopards, buffaloes, rhinoceroses, wart hogs, wild asses, zebras, giraffes, gazelles, and greater and lesser koodoos. He took their pictures with a motion-picture camera which he had improved with a panoramic swiveling device, and which he patented, and formed a company around, as the Akeley Camera. This was used by the Signal Corps in the First World War, during which its creator signed up with the Engineer Corps as a Specialist on Mechanical Devices and Optical Equipment in the Division of Investigation, Research, and Development. Another mechanical device invented by Akeley was the cement gun, which he produced to repair stucco that was peeling on the outside of the Chicago museum. This contrivance, which made use of Akeley's compressed-air-spray method for blowing shellac on animal manikins, was later used in tunnel construction and the lining of irrigation ditches, reservoirs, dams, and so on. It got Akeley another wartime assignment—Special Assistant in the Concrete Department of the Emergency Fleet Corporation.

Akeley liked gorillas, although they tried to kill him, and shot them with regret. (Five of them, all now in an African Hall alcove against a background of seventy-five

thousand artificial leaves and flowers, including an ecolog-
ically unimpeachable blackberry bush that took eight
months to make and cost two thousand dollars.) "I believe
that the gorilla is normally a perfectly amiable and decent
creature," he wrote in 1923 in a book that he pointedly
called *In Brightest Africa.* "I believe that if he attacks
man it is because he is being attacked or thinks he is being
attacked. . . . I believe, however, that the white man who
will allow a gorilla to get within ten feet of him without
shooting is a plain darn fool. . . ." Akeley felt the same
way about elephants, who *also* tried to kill him. "Once
. . . I had such close contact with an old bull up on the
slopes of Mt. Kenya that I had to save myself from being
gored by grabbing his tusks with my hands and swinging
in between them," he wrote in *In Brightest Africa,* and
went on:

> . . . I was suddenly conscious that an elephant was almost on
> top of me. . . . My next mental record is of a tusk right at
> my chest. I grabbed it with my left hand, the other one
> with my right hand, and swinging in between them went to
> the ground on my back. . . . He drove his tusks into the
> ground on either side of me, his curled-up trunk against my
> chest. I had a realization that I was being crushed, and as I
> looked into one wicked little eye above me I knew that I
> could expect no mercy. . . . I heard a wheezy grunt as he
> plunged down and then—oblivion.
> The thing that dazed me was a blow from the elephant's
> trunk as he swung it down to curl it back out of harm's
> way. It broke my nose and tore my cheek open to the teeth.
> . . . When he surged down on me, his big tusks evidently
> struck something in the ground that stopped them. . . . I
> should have been crushed thin as a wafer if his tusks hadn't
> met that resistance—stone, root, or something—underground.

He seems to have thought me dead for he left me. . . . I lay
unconscious for four or five hours. . . . But I did get entirely
over it all, although it took me three months in bed. . . .
The things that stick in my mind are [the elephant's] sagacity,
his versatility, and a certain comradeship which I have never
noticed to the same degree in other animals.

Akeley, who on another occasion killed a leopard bare-
handed, realized that he was in the wrong, morally, vis-à-
vis his African targets. "There is no fun in shooting zebras
and wild asses," he wrote. "It makes one feel uncom-
fortable." A few months after his adventure with the
elephant, which took place in 1911, he found himself in
safer company. His feeling about the matey attitude of
elephants (toward their own kind) had inspired him to
make a bronze group, "The Wounded Comrade," which
showed two elephants helping a wounded bull escape.
"Mr. J. P. Morgan came to the Museum to talk over African Hall," he has written. "I explained the whole plan,
showed him the model of the hall and incidentally The
Wounded Comrade. He liked the scheme. As he left, he
said that he was convinced. 'And,' he added, 'I don't
mind saying,' pointing to the little bronze of The
Wounded Comrade, 'that is what did it.' I shall always
be indebted to Mr. Morgan for that sentence. It gave me
an extraordinary amount of contentment."

This contentment was put to a severe test. The Akeley
plan for an African Hall was okayed by the trustees in
1912, but in 1926, the year of Akeley's death, it was still
on paper. Its originator, who had never *really* recovered
from his bout with the elephant, died in camp, in high

gorilla country in the Belgian Congo, and was buried there. The Museum celebrated his demise with a kind of memorial meeting that no taxonomist could aspire to. The president of the Holland Society, which had conferred its Medal of Award upon Akeley four years earlier, announced that he had now "gone to a higher reward," and read a resolution citing him for having "rescued the natural history of the passing wilds of Africa," and for having "placed it within the grasp of future scientific students of Europe and America . . . for the benefit of [the] intellectual advancement of mankind." Mr. Kermit Roosevelt, a Museum trustee, speaking for his deceased Presidential father and the Boone and Crockett and Explorers Clubs, hailed Akeley as "a man of multifold genius—naturalist, sculptor, engineer, inventor, father of indispensable methods in modern museum exhibition." Professor Osborn, as chairman of the meeting, introduced the Belgian Ambassador, Baron de Cartier de Marchienne, who read a telegram of condolence from Albert, King of the Belgians, and said, in part:

> Akeley, like Saint Francis of Assisi, had a great and kind heart, full of sympathetic understanding for "God's humbler creatures". . . . No doubt King Albert, when planning [the] sanctuary which is called Parç National Albert, was influenced by his . . . experiences. . . . The Parc . . . now embraces the three volcanoes, Visoke, Karissimbi, and Mount Mikeno. . . . Akeley died on the slopes of Mount Mikeno . . . in the midst of the "Sanctuary" which he had planned and which was the realization of one of his fondest dreams. His death was that of a happy warrior who dies on the field of duty in the struggle for the betterment of the world. . . .

Next, Mr. James Earle Fraser, president of the National Sculpture Society, who had made a bas-relief of Morris K. Jesup for the Museum in 1912 and who was to render figures of Daniel Boone, Audubon, Lewis, and Clark, and an equestrian group of Theodore Roosevelt (the Rough Rider on a horse, its bridle reins in the hands of a Negro and an Indian) for the Roosevelt Memorial Building, paid tribute to Akeley's sculpture, including "The Wounded Comrade." *Next*, Osborn introduced Trubee Davison, then Assistant Secretary of War for Air and a trustee. Mr. Davison delivered a speech in which he praised Akeley's qualities as a friend, his cement gun, his camera, and his skill and integrity as a preparator:

> . . . I remember very well sitting with him one day at the Club after luncheon. . . . He was telling me of the projected expedition to Africa to obtain the groups which were to fill that great Hall. I asked him about the specimens that were already available, but that had not yet been mounted. He told me about a compromise that had been suggested in order to overcome the shortage of a bull member of an antelope group, by placing together the skins of two females, and in that way make the whole into a possible resemblance of the male, the falseness of which it was suggested none but an expert might detect. I have never heard any human being flayed as was the individual who made that suggestion. . . .

The meeting concluded with a word from the chairman, who recited a requiem of Robert Louis Stevenson and quoted, or misquoted, another appropriate verse, in this wise:

> Akeley's body lies molding in his grave,
> But his soul goes marching on.

Work on the Akeley African Hall was carried to its conclusion by James L. Clark, *another* Fine Art practitioner in the contemporary mammalian field. Mr. Clark, who is now in his upper eighties and who still drops in at the Museum, first dropped in in 1894, when he was living in Jersey City. "I spent the whole day at the Museum," he recently told a friend. "It was the most wonderful day I ever had. I had never seen anything like it in my life. My next visit was eight years later, when I came to see Dr. Bumpus about a job. He had just been made director; he was a good live wire; he was putting life in the Museum. I was working as an apprentice designer for the Gorham silversmith company in Providence, and studying, nights, at the Rhode Island School of Design, whose director was a friend of Dr. Bumpus, a former professor of comparative anatomy at Brown. Well, Bumpus was an admirer of Akeley, then in Chicago, but Akeley was keeping his taxidermy methods *secret*, and Bumpus asked the School of Design director to recommend a young man who could sculpt animal forms in clay—and perhaps, eventually, learn the Akeley technique. I was recommended! I got the job! Fifty dollars a month—thirty more than I had been getting at Gorham! My first assignment was to model a full-sized bull elk. I had never seen an elk, but I walked across the Park to the Menagerie and studied one. A few months later, when I had made a good many models, including one of the elk, Dr. Bumpus brought a visitor to my room. It was Mr. Akeley! He looked at some of my things, left with Dr. Bumpus, and came back that afternoon, alone, for a chat. Shortly thereafter, he invited me to Chicago for what became a three-months stay. He showed me his secret methods!"

The Akeley invitation was extended, through channels, via a letter from Mr. Hiram N. Higinbotham, president of the Chicago museum and a former Marshall Field partner, to President Jesup. "You may look for Mr. Clark at an early date," Mr. Jesup replied. The American Museum's appreciation of Fine Art is indicated by the fact that a somewhat later date, 1922, found Mr. Clark Assistant to the Director in Full Charge of Preparation; that he subsequently rejoiced in several other resounding titles, among them, Assistant Director (in Full Charge of Preparation), Vice-Director (Preparation and Exhibition), and Assistant Executive Secretary and Assistant Director (General Administration); and that, in these capacities, he received a salary that transcended that of the director himself. "In 1922," he advised his aforementioned friend, "when Professor Osborn asked me to become assistant to the director, and, on Akeley's recommendation, to do African Hall, he offered me a salary of twelve thousand dollars, which was what the director was getting. I asked for fifteen thousand, and the trustees gave me an extra three thousand dollars *secretly*, so as not to seem to give me more than the director."

The director, at this time, was Dr. Lucas, who, after a year's acting-directorship interregnum of Dr. Charles H. Townsend, the director of the Aquarium, had in 1911 bumped Dr. Bumpus. Osborn, as president, had inherited Bumpus as director, but the relationship between the two men was something less than ideal. In 1901, when Bumpus was assistant to the president (Jesup) and Curator of Invertebrate Zoology, Osborn, then second vice-president, Curator of Vertebrate Paleontology, *and* a trustee, had written the live wire, "In order to free the exhibition halls of dust it is very important that cloths should be used rather than feather dusters; in this manner dust is taken out of the Museum instead of being redistributed." And three years later the Curator of Vertebrate Paleontology wrote the director:

> In reply to your note . . . the list of accessions in our department is found on pp. 86 and 95 of my annual report for 1903, carbon of which is in your office. . . . Will you not kindly remember to place notices in the hall directing visitors to your offices? There is a constant string of visitors and book peddlers finding their way into our work rooms.

Thereupon the ex-Brown professor, no stranger to the peremptory note—"My dear Mr. Abramson," he had once written a Museum contractor, "It is only about two hours ago that I saw your cabinet-maker leave the building. Since then two of the chairs have dropped apart"—addressed the ex-Princeton professor as follows:

> On March 21 I wrote you, asking for a list of the accessions to your Department for the year 1903 for use in the Annual Report, and by yours of March 23 I am referred to pp. 86 and 95 of your Annual Report for 1903, a carbon of which you state is in my office.
>
> In reply to this I would say that the statement of the accessions to your Department, if given at all thoroughly in your Annual Report, is so involved with the accessions for 1902 as to make it extremely difficult for a person unacquainted with the facts to prepare a statement similar to that which appeared in the printed Report for the year 1902,

which, by-the-way, you will remember was handed in a year
ago at such a late date as to make it very difficult for us to
issue the completed Report at the time prescribed by our
agreement with the City. I am therefore asking again if you
will not be good enough to kindly have sent to my office a
list similar to that which was printed for the year 1902? . . .
In regard to the last paragraph of your letter, I would say
that the facts are so exaggerated I feel sure it was written
without your knowledge, and I am therefore returning it to
you.

Professor Osborn returned to the fray:

I regret to have delayed sending you the list of accessions
during 1903. I trust it is now all right. . . . As regards the
book agents and visitors in our laboratories, my statement was
made from personal experience. It is not true that there is a
constant succession of interruptions; but it is true that there
are frequent interruptions by visitors who have no business
in the laboratories. I spend comparatively little time there,
but in the last two weeks I have been solicited by a book
agent and an insurance agent. Mr. Granger informed me that
such business is quite frequent, and that there is no way of
keeping these people out.

A few weeks later, the second vice-president, about to
take a holiday, one-upmanned the director with a "My
address while abroad will be: C/o J. S. Morgan & Company, 22 Old Broad Street, London. But I really do not
wish to hear anything about the Museum affairs unless
absolutely necessary."

The champion of the cloth duster had been in the presidential saddle only a couple of years, when, in 1910, he
treated his director to an unexpected six-months' leave of
absence (and Dr. Townsend to his interregnum), at the

end of which Dr. Bumpus redistributed himself as business
manager of the University of Wisconsin. He later became
president of Tufts College (now University). In 1927, he
politely backed away, when, along with more than five
hundred Osborn colleagues and friends from all over the
world, he was invited to contribute his signature to an
illuminated book of greetings to the professor on the occasion of the latter's seventieth birthday. Nor did he show
up at a birthday reception, held in the Museum, of which
the New York *Tribune* wrote:

> While an orchestra played the wedding march, Dr. and Mrs.
> Henry Fairfield Osborn, married forty-six years, marched
> to the dais in the bird room . . . last night to the accompani-
> ment of a rising tribute from one hundred and fifty scientists,
> scholars, and public and financial leaders.
>   Mrs. Osborn blushed like a bride, a brilliant red ostrich
> fan heightening the color. . . .

Five years Osborn's junior, Dr. Bumpus outlived his
ancient foe by eight years, dying, at eighty-one, in 1943.
His death passed unnoticed in the Museum's *Annual Report.*

Frederic A. Lucas, Dr. Bumpus' successor, was, like Professor Bickmore, of New England seafaring stock. His
father was a Plymouth, Massachusetts, clipper ship captain. Starting at the age of six, the son crossed the Atlantic
under parental sail several times, and twice encircled the
globe before going to work in 1871 (when he was eighteen
and The American Museum was two) at Professor Ward's
Natural Science Establishment in Rochester. During his
eleven years there, he prepared a number of specimens for
Professor Joel Allen, who was still at the Agassiz Museum

in Cambridge. "Am sorry that the bird came loose and
only wish that I could hold the perch and screwdriver
both myself," Lucas wrote Allen on a postcard in 1879.
In 1882, he went to the Smithsonian, where he continued
to perform occasional taxidermic chores for Allen, now
at The American Museum. "I shall be glad to undertake the
mounting of the skeleton of the Great Auk at a cost
not to exceed ten dollars, the pedestal to be furnished by
the Am. Mus. Nat. Hist.," he wrote Allen in 1887. By the
time he was tapped by the Am. Mus., at fifty-nine, Lucas
had spent twenty-two years with the Smithsonian (mostly
as a curator of comparative anatomy) and seven years as
curator-in-chief of the Museum of the Brooklyn Institute
of Arts and Sciences, now the Brooklyn Museum. He
was the author of more than three hundred papers, ranging
from "The Berlin Fisheries Exhibit," his first published
work, which he sold to the *Scientific American* for ten
dollars when he was twenty-seven, to a series of studies
of the tongues and skeletons of birds, on which Dr. Robert
Cushman Murphy, Lamont Curator of Birds Emeritus at
The American Museum, has bestowed the accolade:

> In ornithology [Lucas] was among the first in this country
> to turn from the inspection and comparison of skins to more
> fundamental parts of a bird's structure, and a long series of
> papers on the skeletons and soft parts of swifts, humming
> birds, woodpeckers, honey-creepers, titmice, gallinaceous
> birds, *Hesperornis*, and others appeared chiefly between the
> years 1889 and 1900, throwing much new light on the rela-
> tionships of the families and higher groups of birds.
>   An outstanding example of the thoroughness and soundness
> of Doctor Lucas's anatomical investigations is that concerned
> with his views on the affinities of the penguins. When [Leon-

hard] Stejneger, a master zoologist [Dr. Stejneger was a National Museum authority on birds, fish, and reptiles for fifty-nine years], prepared the text on birds for the *Riverside Natural History* (1895), he grouped the penguins as a distinct super-order, equivalent in rank with the ostrich-like birds on the one hand, and with the Euornithes, or carinate birds, on the other. Lucas held strongly against this view. . . . Only in later years was this problem finally settled. . . . The results entirely confirm Lucas's opinion.

Although Professor Osborn got along better with Dr. Lucas than he did with Dr. Bumpus, the Museum's 1919 and 1920 *Annual Reports* suggest that the relationship between the president and the director was, again, something less than ideal. "Our fifty-first annual report is regretfully opened with the statement that the Museum as a whole is now going backward, not forward," Osborn wrote in 1919, and went on:

It is like a grown man confined in the clothing of a youth. . . . This is not said in criticism or complaint of anyone. . . . With all [its] obvious advance, the Museum has certainly come to a full stop in some branches of its educational work, and in many branches *it is actually going backward*. We are not truthfully presenting the facts about amphibians, reptiles, fishes, birds, or mammals—because of disorderly arrangement. In hall after hall the arrangement is less truthful than it was twenty years ago, because the collections are jumbled together out of their natural order. Animals which are not in the least related are placed side by side. Animals of the remote past, in fact of the very dawn of life, crowd the animals of today and yesterday. Small wonder that in the popularized science of the day, which is constantly flowing from Museum sources and finding its way into the newspapers all over this continent, dinosaurs are represented as contemporaneous with the mammoth and the mastodon. Small wonder that the impressions of the superb succession of life through the ages of Vertebrates—of Fishes, of Amphibians, of Reptiles, of Mammals, of the Antiquity of Man—are completely confused. It is exactly as if some Chippendale furniture and Chinese peachblow vases should be placed in the center of an Egyptian hall among the relics and Canopic jars of Queen Thi and the vases of Etruria. This figuratively is the condition of six of our large exhibition halls at the present time. . . . Members and friends must not receive the false impression, through the random completion of an attractive exhibit or habitat group in this or that part of the Museum, that the Museum as a whole is progressing.

Dr. Lucas, who on becoming director had been specifically charged by Dr. Osborn to devote the larger part of his time to the educational arrangement of the exhibition halls, and who had just composed an essay called "Principles of Museum Administration," did not take Osborn's Great Squawk lying down. Drawing, conceivably, on his early nautical experiences, he wrote in the 1920 *Annual Report*:

In the Report for 1919 the President stated that the Museum was going backward; to the Director it would seem that the situation is that of a vessel voyaging through Arctic ice; her progress is impeded; it is not possible to proceed in a direct line, but here and there a lead opens, and by taking advantage of each opportunity that offers, there is steady though slow and indirect progress toward the desired point. Thus it has been with the Museum during the past year; there are many things that we would have liked to do but could not; on the other hand many improvements have been made in all parts of the Museum. For if it be not possible to increase collections on exhibition, it is always possible to improve them by substitution, rearrangement, better methods of display, or, most important of all, by better labeling.

Excellent illustrations of what can be accomplished are shown in the various halls devoted to Mammals. . . . It is pleasant to report that the attendance during the past year has been the largest in the history of the Museum. . . .

The Museum's president did not take *this* lying down. During the next two or three years, his correspondence with his director shows what can happen to a scientist who turns into an administrator. Here are some extracts:

Visiting the Age of Man Hall today, I was surprised to find the two new cases going up without provision being made for interior lighting, which I expressly ordered. . . . I regret to see that the promised effect in the sloth group has not been obtained by the reflectors of the globes. There is great concentration of light at the top and head of the big sloth, while the lower part is insufficiently lighted. . . . It is very important that illumination of the sloth group should be properly adjusted before the glass is put in place. I am beginning to fear that we shall have to call in an expert on illumination from outside. . . . The sloth case must not be the brilliant center of interest in the Hall; it must have only its share of light, as I have repeatedly directed. . . . I have just examined the new model in the Eastern Forest Indian Hall. I regret to say that I do not approve. . . . The male figure must certainly be draped, as the female and girl (*sic*) figures are draped. It seems to be unnatural and unintentionally immodest. Its effect on young people would not be good. It is probable that the Indians divested themselves largely of their clothing while in their tepees . . . but inasmuch as all the female figures are clothed, the male figure should be more or less clothed. . . . I think these otherwise excellent figures should . . . be put in primitive garb; in fact, I direct that this be done. . . . After a clear understanding, according to rules and regulations . . . as to the interior arrangements of the brackets in Mineral Hall [the Morgan Memorial Hall of Minerals and Gems, whose interior was a 1921 gift of George F. Baker] . . . that the brackets should not be placed in a uniform horizontal line, but should be clustered in ovals in certain of the cases, I found on visiting the Hall this afternoon a uniform horizontal line of brackets extending from the door to the center of the Hall. This arrangement . . . will be extremely monotonous. I know it will not please either Mr. Morgan [the son of the memorialee] or Mr. Baker. . . .

Osborn's Mineral Hall letter is stamped "Office of the Director Noted," under which Lucas has written "with regret." On another letter from his chief, beneath its concluding phrase, "The American Museum shall progress or I will retire from office and enjoy a peaceful life," he has written, "And so would we."

Dr. Lucas' progress was impeded, in a way, and his life began to grow more peaceful, at the end of 1923, when he was appointed *honorary* director. He was placed in charge of the Jesup Woods, and died, in 1929, at seventy-six. *De mortuis nil nisi bonum.* "Here [at the Museum], with the aid of William King Gregory [a Museum paleontologist and morphologist, now over ninety and emeritus, who helped Osborn compile his Titanotheres and Proboscidea monographs] and the occasional suggestion of the present writer," Dr. Osborn wrote in the foreword of a posthumously published, Museum-published Lucas autobiography (in which Dr. *Lucas* wrote, "The director of a large museum is frequently, or largely, director in name only"), "he built his most enduring monument, for no one will ever find it necessary or advisable to substantially alter his beautiful and expressive arrangement of the Mammalia and of their characteristic organs. It is a matter of historic justice, therefore, for our Trustees to name this synoptic exhibition Lucas Hall and to associate it per-

petually with the name of a man of fine personal character,
of quaint and persuasive charm, representative of the finest
principles and endowments of the New England character."

Alas, the synoptic hall has lapsed into synonymy and is
now called the Hall of Biology of Mammals.

The man who bumped Dr. Lucas was George H. Sherwood, long assistant (and later executive) secretary of
the Museum and curator-in-chief of its Department of
Education. In 1924, he became acting director and in
1927, director. He had an eye for detail—he had not only
spotted the "aviator" in Osborn's Allen-condolence cable,
but he once returned a check for ten thousand dollars to
an absent-minded, dues-renewing Annual Member with a
note, "You may . . . wish to correct it"—but self-asser-
tion was the last word in his lexicon: he was a director-in-
name-only *par excellence*. "Osborn respected great ability,
and tolerated and encouraged disagreement of his students," Dr. Murphy has said, "but he did require a certain
obedience. Sherwood, a very kindly man, had to kowtow
to him terribly. Lucas, on the other hand, although very
modest, very shy, was firm as a rock."

Although fond of jokes in his personal correspondence,
Sherwood was, officially, grave, deferential, and given to
serious similes. In his first *Annual Report* report as acting
director, he remarked, under the heading "Administration,
Operation, and Building," "Our service departments include the Director's office, which is responsible for the
carrying out of the policies determined by the President
and the Board of Trustees and for the general administration of the Museum," and went on to define the duties of

the bursar's office, the registrar's office, the office of the superintendent of the building, the Department of Construction and Repairs, and the Department of Heating and Lighting. As director, unlike his predecessor, he did not issue a director's report in the *Annual Report*, but, in his first full directorial year, he *did* submit a statement, under "Educational and Scientific Reports," which compared the Museum not to an ice-breaker but to a sky-scraper:

> The mushroom-like rapidity with which a modern skyscraper takes shape fills us with astonishment, and we can hardly believe our eyes, as daily we see tons and tons of steel girders arise, story upon story. In viewing this modern miracle, too often we forget the months and months of close, painstaking work in the drafting rooms, with rule, caliper, and micrometer. So it is in building the American Museum: it is the explorations and the research that constitute the foundation and the mighty supporting structure of the American Museum. . . .

The *president's* report, that year, started off with a quotation from the Bible ("And David said to Solomon his son . . ."). Osborn was fond of apt quotations. As he warmed up in office, he gave his presidential reports titles like "The American Museum Ideal," "The American Museum and Education," "The American Museum and Citizenship," "The American Museum and Defeatism," and "The American Museum and the World," and launched them with more or less appropriate citations from Shakespeare, Francis Bacon, Washington, Jefferson, Lincoln, Theodore Roosevelt, Joffre, Foch, Cicero, Agassiz, Thomas Carlyle, Samuel J. Tilden, and himself. He then

had his reports bound up separately and sent to several
hundred educational institutions, libraries, museums, and
American Museum members (who had, of course, already
received them in the *Annual Report*).

Well, back, at long last, to Mr. Clark, the directorial
assistant (in full charge of preparation) whose services
the trustees, *in camera*, valued twenty-five per cent more
highly than those of the director. (Osborn was no stranger
to financial secrecy; after his first few years at the Museum, he took no salary, but he received a secret annual
allowance of sixteen thousand dollars from Uncle Pierpont
for his fossil department. This bounty did not show up in
the Museum's books, and, when discovered by Mr. Beards-
ley Ruml, at a time when he was looking into the Museum's economy in connection with a requested grant
from the Spelman Fund of New York, of which he was a
trustee, caused him to raise his eyebrows. Dr. Lucas, come
to think of it, may have been more privy to financial
secrecy than Mr. Clark supposed; he once wrote Osborn
a letter in which he "respectfully" suggested "that it would
be no more than fair that I should receive . . . the difference between Mr. Clark's . . . salary and mine.") In
terms of réclame for the Museum, Clark earned his pay.
He visited taxidermists all over the country, recruiting
and training them until he had built up a staff of fifty
hand-picked men. Besides African Hall, he supervised the
mounting of (and in some cases mounted himself) the
habitat groups for two other spectacular mammal exhibits, both of which, like the Akeley Hall, are still Museum cynosures. The first of these to open—in 1930—and
the first hall wholly occupied by habitat groups especially

designed for it, was the Vernay-Faunthorpe Hall of South
Asiatic Mammals—eighteen alcoves, arranged around a
pair of Indian elephants in the middle of the hall. The
alcoves' lions, tigers, rhinoceroses, deer, antelopes, water
buffalo, and so on were collected in India, Burma, and
Siam in the 1920s by Arthur S. Vernay, a rich English
antique-furniture dealer, orchid raiser, flamingo fancier,
and big-game hunter, who, accompanied by Clark preparators and artists, conducted fifteen expeditions for the
Museum and became a trustee thereof; and by a friend
of his, Colonel John C. Faunthorpe, the British Resident
Commissioner of Lucknow, India. In 1942, six years after
the dedication of African Hall, the North American Hall
of Mammals, the third great Clark-directed attraction,
opened, thus giving to the public, in this war year, what
the Museum's director, Dr. Albert E. Parr, called "a
most timely opportunity to receive an inspiring impression
not only of the animals of our land, but also of the rich
and varied beauty of the country we must defend." This
hall boasts *twenty-eight* alcoves, spearheaded by ones fea-
turing the Osborn Caribou and the Grant Caribou,
named (by Museum scientists) after trustees Osborn and
Madison Grant. Other alcoves contain white sheep and
mule deer whose exhibit inscriptions proclaim them "collected and presented by Mr. and Mrs. Richard K. Mellon,"
white tail deer (Mr. and Mrs. E. H. Harriman), bighorn
sheep (Mr. and Mrs. Henry P. Davison), jaguar (Cornelius
Vanderbilt Whitney), and musk-ox, or oxen, which had
been lying around the Museum, unmounted, since the old
Peary days and were finally brought to life, so to speak,
by Mr. Clark and his crew. These halls, as a by-product,

have introduced botany as well as mammalogy; vegetation appropriate to the exhibits' backgrounds is provided and labeled—or, in some cases, omitted, indicating erosion.

Mr. Clark, although on the Museum's payroll, did not confine his activities to the institution. On the side, at the time when he was appointed Dr. Lucas' titular assistant ("Not only have I had no assistance [from him] so far but there has been an unusual amount of [preparation] work which has called for my personal supervision," Lucas wrote Osborn in 1922), he was vice-president and general manager of the Akeley Camera Company, which had a factory in West Seventeenth Street. He became the company's president after Akeley's death. "I was also running the James L. Clark Studio for mounting animals," he has said, "which I had established in 1910 near the Bronx Zoo, so as to be near live animals, for purposes of study. This studio was the biggest and best thing of its kind. I had a staff of twenty or more; our clients were museums and big-game hunters like Theodore Roosevelt, for whom we prepared personal trophies as well as his white rhinoceros, hartebeest, and ostrich, which he shot in Africa and which are now in the Smithsonian. I sometimes had $600,-000's worth of business in the house. I wound the place up in 1941, after thirty-one years. Professor Osborn allowed me to keep it, and the camera business, going while I was working for him. Along with lectures I gave on five African trips I made for the Museum, *and* my Museum salary, these activities made me well off. I got out of the stock market in 1928, just before the Depression. The professor was a marvelous man. He used to wear a working smock around the Museum."

The successful moonlighter, whom I really ought to call *Dr.* Clark (he never went to college, but Wesleyan College gave him a D.Sc. in 1933), now bears the title of Director Emeritus, Preparation and Installation, in the Museum's Department of Exhibition and Graphic Arts. He is still fond of secrets. In a recently published book, *Good Hunting: Fifty Years of Collecting and Preparing Habitat Groups for the American Museum,* he writes, apropos a lunch given in 1930 at the Knickerbocker Club by Mr. Vernay "for his personal friends, hunters, museum staff members, and others in appreciation of their interest and for what they had done to help make his South Asiatic Hall such a success":

. . . When the luncheon finally broke up, I rose to take a stretch and casually walked over to a window to observe the green trees in Central Park. As I stood there, a middle-aged man walked up to me and said, "You know I would like to go on an expedition some day." Having no idea who he was, I talked briefly with him, asking him to come over to the museum some time to discuss it. And in a week or so he walked into my office.

Because I had had so many similar requests, both in person and by mail from people wanting to go on an expedition, I simplified my dilemma by using the questionnaire that I had made up earlier and had used down through the years. One of the questions I listed was: "Could you donate to the Museum Expedition a sum of money to help pay your expenses? If so, how much?" Since this fellow's name meant nothing to me and since he had volunteered nothing very constructive, I gave him a questionnaire to fill out and bring in to me in a week or so. Again he returned in due time, and, sheepishly laying the questionnaire on my desk, said, "If that sum isn't enough I can get more." Hastily I opened the paper to where this particular question appeared, and I fear

I must have gulped when I read "fifty thousand dollars."
But I quickly collected myself and said, "I think that will
be enough."

This resulted in one of the most interesting expeditions
of my long experience, a trip to the very heart of Africa
in the very remote area of southern Sudan. . . . Here we
would find the giant eland, the largest of all antelope. . . .
We had long wanted a group of these fine animals. . . .
Because of the importance of this group and my past experience in this Central African region, the administration approved of my going and taking my sponsor with me.

Good hunting in the book's index, which illuminates
this passage with a name, reveals that the sheepish sponsor
was Mr. C. Oliver O'Donnell, who in due time (about
ten minutes) became an Associate Founder.

Another secret in the text proper of *Good Hunting*
is embedded in a passage dealing with a 1929 Clark expedition to get lions for the African Hall:

This lion group and the expedition to collect it was financed
by a husband and wife who wanted to see Africa, take
pictures, but do no shooting. Since the wife would be the
only woman in the party and since she knew that Mrs. Clark
had had the experience of an African safari, she invited her
to go along as her guest and companion. . . . It was most
unfortunate that, not long after we took to the field, the
relations between the two women became strained (not an
uncommon occurrence on a long safari), and to avoid an
open rupture, Mrs. Clark agreed to withdraw quietly from
the safari. . . .

No mention, again, of the sponsorial name, but, if del-
icacy prompted this omission, it did not extend, altogether,
to the voluble index, which, referring to the relevant

pages, reads "Carlisle, Mr. and Mrs. (sponsors of African expedition)." An inscription in African Hall is more explicit; it reads, "Lion Group: Mr. and Mrs. J. Lister Carlisle." And another engraved label commemorates the anonymous philanthropist of the Knickerbocker Club: "Giant Eland Group: C. Oliver O'Donnell."

Other acknowledgements in this hall and the North American one, bearing as they do the names of such donors and expedition backers as (in addition to those cited) Daniel E. Pomeroy, Richard Archbold, Max Fleischmann, and George Eastman, reflect a bygone period in which economic royalists were enthusiastic about Museum safaris, on many of which many of them went along. One of the most productive *non*-rich collectors for these halls, and others, was T. Donald Carter, who joined the Museum staff in 1920 and is now Curator Emeritus of Mammalogy. Mr. Carter's Museum bag, the fruit of thirty-two expeditions undertaken between 1928 and 1959 (six in Africa, one in South America, one in West China, one in Indo-China, and the rest in North America), is well up in the thousands. A student of the Museum recently went on a small expedition with *him*, around North American Hall. Carter paused before the black bear group to point out a water moccasin in the foreground. "The Museum wanted me to bring back one alive for taxidermy," he said. "I got this fellow in Florida, and drove him back in a convertible with my sister and my mother. We had to leave the car open; if we closed it, in the heat, the snake would have died. So one of us always had to snakesit at lunch." He led the way on to the fisher and porcupine group. "My sister got the porcupine under a ladies' outhouse at Mount Washington," he said. "When I came here, Dr. Allen was still alive. He lived in a hotel near Amsterdam Avenue and Ninety-second Street. He was over eighty, and he liked to study small mammals at home. I'd take heavy suitcases of specimens to him in the trolley. He told me to use taxis, but George N. Pindar, the registrar, who was in charge of petty expenses, didn't go for this. I'm glad I came to the Museum when I did. In those days, a small group was interested in the place as a whole. Now, everyone is a specialist. Some people here are just interested in bats!"

The results of the expeditions undertaken by Carter, Clark, Akeley, and others were not always regarded by their colleagues as precisely scientific, since—some of the curators felt—the chief thing that came out of them was a kind of mounted zoo, botanical labels or no botanical labels. However, the publicity in the press that Professor Osborn wanted shut off from young people was terrific, especially in the case of big game from far-off continents. In the early 1940s, when the war had put a stop to geographical exploration, and when the Museum, its staff crippled by this conflict and by Depression-bred expulsions and resignations (salaries had been cut in the 1930s), was floundering around in a kind of post-Depression depression of its own, the trustees, hoping for guidance, asked Dr. Clark Wissler, who had just retired as Curator of Anthropology but was still *in situ* emeritus, to write a critical historical survey of the institution. Dr. Wissler had been surveying the Museum, out of a corner of his eye, for forty years. He was an authority on the American Indian, on whom he had written several books. (These have been credited with reflecting a pioneering recognition of the importance of the psychological element in anthropological research—a point of view that has been more outspokenly emphasized by Dr. Margaret Mead, who, as an ethnology curator, has been writing *her* books at the Museum for *more* than forty years.) Dr. Wissler was also, at least in the Indian field, a man of remarkable financial judgment. In 1910, when a collection of three hundred and sixty-eight paintings and fifty sketches by George Catlin—mostly of Plains Indians—was offered to the Museum by Miss Elizabeth Catlin, one of the artist's daughters, for twenty-five thousand dollars, Wissler advised the Museum to make a bid of ten thousand dollars for them. Dr. Lucas voted against this, on the grounds that "the price . . . is very large in proportion to their value," but President Osborn overruled him, and, moreover, got Ogden Mills to put up the ten thousand, which Miss Catlin accepted. For half a century, the collection's headquarters was a storage room. In 1954, the Museum sold the Catlins—minus a score or so which it kept to draw upon for Indian-hall backgrounds—to the Kenedy Gallery, as agent for Paul Mellon, for four hundred and fifty thousand dollars. This transaction, suggested to him by President White, had received the blessing of Dr. Wissler's successor, Dr. Harry L. Shapiro. "My first reaction was no," he has said. "I was reluctant to let the Catlins go. But we couldn't use more than a handful of them in exhibitions, and their scientific value was minimal. Furthermore, they were a considerable expense. They were often sent out on loan, and this takes a lot of your time, with bookkeeping at both ends. I stipulated that part of

the income go to set up research scholarships for anthropology students who had just finished graduate work
and were about to become low man, or low men, on
the totem pole at a university. These give their recipients
a year of freedom before they get caught up in the
academic business. We've kept about twenty-five of the
Catlins—those having the greatest anthropological interest."

For all his savvy about Indians and pictures of Indians,
Dr. Wissler, as a museum historian, may have been a bit
tendentious. Like many of the Museum's anthropologists
(whose department currently lists twenty names), con-
cerning themselves as they do with *people*, he had a
slightly patronizing attitude toward those of his colleagues
who dealt in animals. (Staff anthropologists today have
their own lunch table, presided over by Dr. Shapiro, in
the curators' section of the employees' cafeteria, where
they nod politely to the zoologists.) The Wissler survey,
which rambled along for four hundred typewritten pages,
inclined toward the anti-Akeley, anti-mounted-zoo, philosophy. It observed, a trifle sourly, that big-game mammals,
favored in exhibits, "may be threatened by improved zoo
techniques"; that curators, in the 1920s, were expected
to be "outdoor men"; that preparation men outranked
the heads of scientific departments; that publication and
research had often been curtailed in the past ("The [De-
partment of Anthropology] staff members and their associates have published or prepared twelve papers, and it
is a matter of great regret that funds are not immediately
available for the printing of those awaiting publication,"
the surveyor had written in the *Annual Report* for 1926,

a year in which the Museum had received bequests of over three million dollars); and that data and collections had piled up, unstudied, while the Museum went on to more and more "publicity explorations."

Before going on, or back, to the greatest publicity explorer of all, Dr. Roy Chapman Andrews (another of Dr. Wissler's implied targets), let us first backtrack, a good deal further, into a curious episode involving Professor Osborn that took place *before* he became president.

5

On FEBRUARY 27, 1906, Dr. Samuel P. Langley, the third secretary of the Smithsonian Institution, died. The regents of the Smithsonian appointed as acting secretary Mr. Richard Rathbun, an authority on marine invertebrates who was in charge of the National Museum, and started to cast about for a successor to Dr. Langley. In May, after reading an article in the New York *Evening Post* that included his name on a list of candidates, Professor Osborn sent a telegram to Mr. John B. Henderson, a former senator from Missouri and chairman of the Regents' Executive Committee:

> . . . I respectfully withhold my name as a candidate because my present plan of scientific researches and publications for the Geological Survey [the Titanotheres monograph] and the American Museum would prevent acceptance even if the very high honor of a call should happen to come to me. I trust you will kindly make known to the Board that I am not on the list of candidates.

In November, Dr. Alexander Graham Bell, the Pooh Bah of the Smithsonian's regents, urged the professor to reconsider. "Of course I can give you no assurance beforehand that in any event you will be elected," he wrote, but he also wrote, "The Secretary of the Smithsonian Institution stands before the world as the representative of Pure Science in America. . . . If there is no hope of our obtaining a man of your eminence in the scientific world, there is serious danger of the position being degraded to that of a mere administrative officer, and Pure Science in America will suffer."

Osborn apparently concluded that he would not come to the rescue of Pure Science. "I have positively decided that my original decision was a wise one," he wrote Dr. Bell, and adduced, in support of it, his feeling that the Smithsonian post would interfere with his "very large program of exploration and publication." He had, he stated, "in various stages of completion," "two monographs for the Geological survey, two books, and a large number of special memoirs, such as that upon the evolution of the horse."

The inventor of the telephone did not take two noes for an answer. A few days later, he buttonholed Osborn at a meeting of the National Academy of Sciences in Boston and assured him that the regents especially desired an investigator as well as an administrator, and that the secretary would be encouraged to continue his scientific researches. This chat seems to have encouraged *Dr. Bell*, at least, since following it he wired Osborn, "The interests of science in America are at stake and I would urge an immediate reply confirming our verbal understanding in

Boston." However, this telegram crossed a letter from
Osborn that contained another no—"My chief scientific
duty lies here in New York. . . . This high post . . .
would make a serious break in my line of investigation"—
and suggested the election of Dr. Charles T. Walcott, an
eminent geologist.

The regents of the Smithsonian did not take *three* noes
for an answer. On December 4, they unanimously elected
Osborn secretary; telegrams to this effect were sent to
him by Dr. Bell and by the Institution's chancellor, Melville W. Fuller, the Chief Justice of the United States.
The papers were full of the news. "Scientific men of
Washington are congratulating themselves upon the acquisition of so distinguished a man in the scientific world
as an addition to the local colony. . . . Prof. Osborn is
a native of Ohio, having been born in Cincinnati forty-
nine years ago," the Washington *Post* declared, and ran
a picture of someone else. "A worthy successor to Henry
and Langley," said the Boston *Transcript*. During the next
few days, the nominee received over a hundred messages
of congratulation. One of the first to come in was from a
member of the local colony, Cleveland Abbe, a research
observer of the U. S. Weather Bureau, who, after felicitat-
ing Osborn, offered to sell or lease him his house in
Washington. Purer expressions of congratulation were dispatched by Theodore Roosevelt, then President; Nicholas
Murray Butler; many members of the Smithsonian staff;
the scientific staff of the American Museum; and Fairfield
Osborn, now president of the New York Zoological Society and then a Princeton sophomore, who sent a tele-

gram "from your admiring Son" and at the same time wrote his other parent:

> Dear Marm,
>
> Isn't it splendid about Papa? What does it mean? I was never so surprised in my life, because you remember your remark of how there was no chance of Papa's accepting it. . . .

The regents' choice appears to have wavered. "I shall take [the invitation] into most earnest consideration and hope to reach a decision in the course of a few days," he wrote Chancellor Fuller on December 5, and he drew up a statement for the newspapers that ran in part, "The invitation to cooperate in this work is very tempting and I am carefully considering it. . . . Yesterday's action by the Regents has taken me completely by surprise. I now feel bound to reconsider the matter because the invitation comes in such a generous and kindly spirit." This period of deliberation was punctuated by a serious phone call. In an undated, penciled, interoffice note (which is listed in Central Files as having been written between December 5 and December 11), Osborn read, *"Please call up 672 Madison* [Avenue] for a message from J. Pierpont Morgan." Under this, is Osborn's handwriting, in red crayon, there appears the notation, "Strongly advises against acceptance."

On December 11, thirteen months before the death of President Morris K. Jesup and at the end of a week during which the press all over the country was running eulogistic editorials about the new secretary, the minuet came to an end. That day, Osborn wrote the chancellor a letter that covered a good deal of ground, without, however, mentioning Uncle Pierpont.

> The most honorable post of Secretary of the Smithsonian Institution . . . is the greatest honor I have received or expect to receive [this ran in part]. I consider it, moreover, a call to the service of my country. . . . After several days which I have devoted almost exclusively to reflection on this matter from every standpoint I find myself unable to accept your invitation. . . . Acceptance would involve a change of career just at a time when I am trying to publish the results of thirty years of research. . . . For the past sixteen years . . . I have been interrupted and drawn away by executive and administrative work of the *very* character which would be demanded of your new Secretary on a grander scale. . . . The opportunity [for paleontological research] could not be recreated in Washington because it is in a branch of pure science which least of all bears upon human welfare and happiness and is, moreover, enormously expensive. . . . A change of residence would cut me off from my materials of research. . . .

No sooner had the axe fallen on Pure Science in the nation's capital than Professor Osborn received another round of congratulatory messages—this time, for declining the secretaryship and remaining at his post. In January, 1907, Dr. Walcott became the fourth secretary of the Smithsonian, and a year later Professor Osborn became the fourth president of The American Museum. He had, by this time, amplified his *Who's Who in America* entry with a line reading "elected sec. Smithsonian Instn., Dec. 4, 1906, but declined," and this abortive election has since been more enduringly enshrined in his write-up in the Dictionary of American Biography.

6

"ROY CHAPMAN ANDREWS was born here," the Columbia Encyclopedia states in its four-sentence account of Beloit, Wisconsin, after drawing attention to such other local assets as shoes, paper-making and wood-working machinery, diesel engines, electrical equipment, winter sports, and Beloit College (coeducational). The Museum's most celebrated staff explorer (Akeley was a free-lance, not on salary) was a striking victim of the not unfamiliar process whereby a valuable museum field man or indoor researcher is turned in middle life into a somewhat less valuable administrator. Cast out, in his prime, after less than seven years as director, by the institution whose fame he had increased and to whose collections his expeditions had contributed more than ten thousand paleontological treasures, including many hitherto unknown to science, Andrews spent his remaining nineteen years in semiretirement in Connecticut and California, rehashing his early experiences in popular books, several of them written for chil-

dren. He died at seventy-six in Carmel, in 1960. The
Encyclopaedia Britannica (as well as the Columbia, under
a separate biographical listing) has been delighted to honor
him, but his death passed unnoticed in the Museum's *Annual Report*. "Roy was a peculiar fellow," Dr. Murphy
has said. "He was full of hiatuses in his knowledge. He
was exposed to a great many things that never took. He
didn't know whether he believed in the inheritance
of acquired characters or not." Superficial, enthusiastic,
personable, brave, a great field-trip organizer and a mar-
velous public-relations man and money raiser in the years
immediately preceding the Depression, Andrews produced
only one or two scientific papers but twenty-two books,
none of them very scientific and many of them crisscrossed
with identical passages. What made him tick? His *Ends
of the Earth*, published in 1929, starts out revealingly
enough:

> Almost every day someone asks me: "How did you start
> exploring and digging up dinosaur eggs in the Gobi Desert?"
> I can answer simply enough: "I couldn't help it. I happen
> to have been born to do it. I am sure that I would have
> been a rotten failure doing anything else."
> Ever since I can remember, I always intended to be a
> naturalist and explorer. Nothing else ever had a place in my
> mind. My first shotgun was given to me when I was nine. . . .
> Every moment that I could steal from school was spent in
> the woods along the banks of Rock River or on the water
> itself. . . . Taxidermy was a necessity, so I taught myself from
> books. . . . To enter the American Museum of Natural His-
> tory was my life ambition. . . .

Andrews' Bachelor of Arts degree, conferred by Beloit
College in 1906 (Beloit and Brown gave him honorary

degrees two decades later, when he was at the height of
his expeditionary fame), was only a few weeks old when
he gained the office of Mr. George H. Sherwood, then
an assistant to Dr. Bumpus and later his successor. Sherwood passed his visitor along to the director, who at
first shook his head, and then, suitably entreated ("You
have to have someone to scrub the floors, don't you?"),
nodded.

> . . . Never before or since have I been as happy [Andrews
> wrote many years later]. The day I was introduced to Frank
> Chapman I nearly suffocated with delight. He had written my
> bible, the "Handbook of North American Birds." I used to
> hang about the meteorites in the foyer at one o'clock to get
> a sight of Professor Osborn when he went to luncheon. I
> never really hoped to meet him.

The floors that the young hero-worshiper was permitted
to scrub were those of the taxidermy department, and
his first close Museum contact was James L. Clark, then
rounding out his fourth year as a budding Fine Art
practitioner. Both men were twenty-two. Clark got Andrews into whales. He enlisted his help on the construction
of a wire-netting-and-papier-mâché model of a seventy-
six-foot sulphur-bottom whale, which was a Museum fix-
ture for sixty years. It has recently been bumped by a
ninety-four-foot, fiberglass-and-plastic whale in the new
Hall of Ocean Life. Andrews' second whale assignment
came in the winter of 1907. A fifty-four-foot North
Atlantic right whale had been harpooned and beached at
Amagansett, Long Island, and Clark, instructed by Bumpus
to buy it and bring back its bones, took Andrews along.
"I was the most excited and the proudest boy in all New

York State as we journeyed toward Amagansett," Andrews has written. "Only seven months in the Museum and off on an expedition!" The expedition, which achieved its purpose, confirmed him in an interest in cetology. During the next seven years, he collected, photographed, measured, and took notes on whales in Alaska, British Columbia, Korea, and Japan. In New York, between trips, he lectured on and wrote about whales ("It was almost indecent the way I spied upon their private lives. . . . I even went so far as to crawl into the tummies of several just to see what sort of apartments Jonah had rented"), and he also developed into a general lecturer and popularizer. He was accompanied in Japan by a native lantern-slide colorist, with whom he investigated Japanese home life and the beauties of nature, and back at *his* home (he had a penthouse in the Hotel des Artistes, not far from the Museum), he held forth at ladies' clubs on "Camera Hunting for Whales," "The Wilderness of Northern Korea," and "Beauty Spots of Japan." Andrews talked about whales so much, both publicly and privately, that a New Bedford friend of his sent him a book about them. For all his Biblical-real-estate approach toward whales, the curator's reaction to this was more scientific than literary. "I read very carefully the book you have sent me some time ago called 'Moby Dick' by Melville," he wrote his friend, and went on:

> and am surprised to see how much all New Bedford people seem to think of him. Some parts of it seem to me to be good, but as a whole I think it is uninteresting and tremendously inaccurate in many parts. The story would be good if about one-third of it were cut out and Melville had

learned something about whales before he tried to write it. He seems to know nothing whatever about the anatomy and very little of the natural history of whales. He even contends that whales are fish which, at the time this book was written, was known pretty well by everyone to be erroneous. I presume its appeal to New Bedford people is because it does give a good picture of New Bedford during the time of whale days. From the standpoint of the whale, the "Cruise of the Cachalot" by Bullen is a good deal better, I think, and he knows a good deal more about whales than Melville did. These critical comments, however are for you alone, so don't get me in "bad" with the other whalemen up there by reading this letter in one of your "gams" about the stove.

Around 1915, Andrews, now Assistant Curator of Mammalogy, stopped talking about whales and started talking about Central Asia. He found a sympathetic ear in President Osborn, who in 1900 had prophesied that this area would be found to be the birthplace of primitive man. Dr. Matthew, the Curator of Vertebrate Paleontology, had strung along with this theory, and both men also believed that Central Asia was the place of origin of many non-human mammals which had later migrated to Europe and America. Encouraged by these colleagues, Andrews, by 1920, had made a couple of reconnoitering trips in the neighborhood of Mongolia. The next year, after personally raising most of the money for its initial stage, he organized what was called the Third Asiatic Expedition, which carried on, with interruptions, for nearly a decade. It was far and away the most ambitious such venture ever undertaken. With headquarters established in Peking, it employed an army of Museum and Museum-connected paleontologists, paleobotanists, archeologists, zoologists, topographers, herpetologists, surgeons, and geologists (the famous French priest, Teilhard de Chardin, was one, in 1930), who pioneeringly traversed the Gobi in fleets of motorcars; it spent close to a million dollars; it coped with bandits, a treacherous terrain, and the vagaries of Chinese officials. It never did discover primitive man, although for a while the Museum hinted that the Osborn-Matthew theory was correct. "The Expeditions found evidences of prehistoric man but no fossil bones," Dr. Chester A. Reeds, the Curator of Geology and Invertebrate Paleontology, wrote in a Museum publication. ". . . At various places along the southern margin of the desert . . . superficial traces of one or two prehistoric cultures were observed. On the north side of the Altai Mountains, where workable artifact materials such as jasper, chalcedony and agate exist, there were abundant evidences of long-standing human occupation." Taking its cue, perhaps, from the Museum, the Encyclopaedia Britannica stated in 1929, "The expeditions discovered . . . extensive evidence of primitive human life on the Central Asian plateau," but it dropped this claim in a later edition. The expedition did produce, however, a dazzling succession of non-human fossils, including the skull and other parts of the Baluchitherium, a tree-browsing rhinoceros that was the largest known land mammal, as well as the dinosaur eggs that got the Museum on the first page of newspapers all over the world. The first batch of these— twenty-five, after bits of their shells, embedded in sandstone, had been assembled—was found in the summer of 1923. The eggs were identified as dinosaurian by Dr. Walter Granger, Andrews' second-in-command, chief paleontologist, and, in fact, the scientific backbone of the expedition. (Andrews never had much idea of what he was looking at, scientifically speaking.) News of their discovery so electrified Professor Osborn that, accompanied by his wife, he at once took off for the Gobi. Change of scene did not impair the commanding powers of the president of the American Museum. "Professor Osborn was exceedingly interested in a specimen which I had found at Irdin Manha," Dr. Andrews wrote later, and went on:

It was a single premolar tooth, representing an archaic group of mammals known as the Amblypoda. . . . This single upper premolar tooth was the only specimen of the group we had discovered in two years' search. Professor Osborn considered it so important that he asked to be taken to the bench, about two miles from camp, and to have me photographed on the spot where I had picked up the tooth.

Later we drove ten miles down the valley and stopped for tiffin. As we were returning, Professor Osborn pointed to a low, sandy exposure a half mile away, and said:

"Have you prospected that knoll?"

"No," I said, "it is the only one in the basin that we have not examined. It seemed too small to bother about."

"I don't know why," said the Professor, "but I would like to have a look at it. Do you mind running over?"

When we stopped at the base of the hillock, I did not leave the car, but Professor Osborn and Granger walked out to examine the exposure. As he left, the Professor turned to me and said with a smile:

"I am going to find another coryphodont tooth."

Two minutes later he waved his arms and shouted, "I have it—another tooth!"

I could hardly believe my eyes and ears. Jumping out of the car, I ran to the spot. The tooth that I had found was the third or fourth upper premolar of the right side. The one Professor Osborn had discovered was the third or fourth premolar of the left side, and of almost exactly the same size.

Naturally they could not have been from the same specimen, as the two had been found eight miles apart. These are the facts. The explanation of this remarkable telepathic coincidence is left to the psychologist.

Back in New York, the eggs, which were respectfully examined at a trustees' meeting attended by Messrs. Pyne, Grant, Felix Warburg, Cleveland H. Dodge, Ogden L. Mills, and other amateur oölogists, helped Andrews, in the course of lectures and personal solicitations which he made in the winter of 1923–24, raise two hundred and eighty-four thousand dollars for further Gobi excavation. An egg that particularly helped him locally was one that was bought for five thousand dollars by a member of the Colgate soap family and presented to Colgate University. This purchase, enthusiastically reported in the press, proved, however, something of a boomerang abroad. The Chinese government got the idea that dinosaur eggs were *worth* five thousand dollars apiece, and the Museum's subsequent disclaimer and concomitant announcement that the Colgate-egg price was a fictitious one, arrived at for reasons of publicity, fell on deaf ears in Peking. In 1925, a great many more eggs were moved from the Gobi to Central Park West. A projected 1926 expedition was called off because of civil wars in China, and four years later the expedition wound up. The events that led to its demise have been well described by President Osborn in an *Annual Report:*

> It is most unfortunate that when the Nationalist party assumed control of a large part of China in 1928 the movement was accompanied by an outburst of anti-foreign feeling. When the Expedition returned to Kalgan that year, an unofficial body

known as the Cultural Society of Peking directed the Governor of Chahar Province to confiscate its collections. The Society then proceeded to inflame the public by publishing disparaging and untruthful articles about the Expedition, stating that it had been "searching for oils and minerals," that its members were "spies against the Chinese Government" and were "stealing Chinese priceless treasures." The Expedition's collections were released after six weeks' negotiations, but from that time on, diplomatic arrangements with the Chinese for the continuance of the Expedition became increasingly difficult. In spite of the efforts of President Osborn, Secretary of State Stimson, and Leader Roy Chapman Andrews, it was possible to make arrangements for only one more expedition, namely, in the year 1930. Eventually the opposition developed to such formidable proportions that it was considered not worth while to spend further time and money in attempting to combat such obstruction. Doctor Andrews, therefore, was instructed to close the headquarters of the Expedition in Peking. . . .

Mongolia is now behind the Iron Curtain. The Museum would like to duck under this curtain, and get back to the Gobi, and it has extended appropriate feelers, but nothing has come of them. In the summer of 1964, however, Dr. Malcolm C. McKenna, then an associate curator and now Frick Associate Curator of Vertebrate Paleontology (as such, he is sorting out an unrivaled collection of North American fossil mammals which Childs Frick, a longtime trustee, left the Museum, along with an endowment of seven and a half million dollars, in 1965), spent eleven days in the Gobi, unofficially. "I went there because the Andrews expeditions—the largest privately endowed land expeditions ever to leave the United States—brought the Museum an immense collection of Mesozoic fossils, some of which are now being studied for the first time," he said on his return. "No one from here had been to Mongolia since his trips, and the younger men, like me, don't know, or didn't know, what it looks like, geologically speaking. I wanted to find out more about the local rocks and sediments. The United States doesn't recognize the Mongolian People's Republic, and my wife and I had to go in as tourists. No collecting. We visited some areas of extreme interest. We penetrated southwestern Mongolia as far as the south side of the Artsa Bogdo Range, about a hundred and fifty miles from the Chinese border; Andrews had been there in 1925. We took hundreds of notes and hundreds of slides, including color photographs of the old Andrews expedition sites in the so-called Gobi Desert—the word 'gobi' is merely the Mongol term for a long, flat valley between mountain ranges; the phrase 'Gobi Desert' is tautological. I got the sort of background data that we need in studying our collection of fossil remains, and I'm corresponding with a Mongolian scientist, Demberelyin Dashzeveg, in the hope of setting up another expedition there sometime." Nothing has come of this correspondence. The Russians have done some profitable digging in the Gobi, post-Andrews, and not long ago a team from the Warsaw Institute of Paleozoology brought back thirty-five tons of Mongolian fossils, including the skull of a one-hundred-and-twenty-five-million-year-old reptile which Dr. McKenna, with the freemasonry of paleozoologists, has mounted for the Polish institute.

The Central Asiatic expeditions marked the peak of the Museum's period of great explorations. A couple of years after the Gobi was declared off bounds to Central Park

West, the Depression set in in earnest, putting an end to field expeditions other than those supported by special endowments; Professor Osborn, the ardent champion of big-game and big-fossil excursions, retired, at seventy-five, as president; and his chair was filled by a non-scientist, F. Trubee Davison, a trustee and the son of a late trustee and Morgan partner, who brightened up the *Annual Reports* with no references to Shakespeare (or himself), but, on occasion, to "Mother Nature." (*His* successor, Mr. Alexander M. White, an investment banker, in *his* reports, saluted not Mother Nature but the management-consultant firm of Cresap, McCormick & Paget, whose services he retained, on taking office in 1951, "to prepare an objective study of our entire operation and to point out ways, if any, in which we might conduct our affairs more efficiently.") In 1934, Mr. Sherwood, the third consecutive director to abandon this title on request, was bumped by Dr. Andrews, then a co-vice-director with his old whale-retrieving companion, Mr. Clark. The new director was more of an outdoors man than an indoors man; he missed the Gobi; he was not happy as an administrator. One of the things that he enjoyed while in office, however, was a series of seafood lunches held every Monday in the fifth-floor laboratory of the Department of Vertebrate Paleontology. These originated, in 1936, with Mr. Louis Monaco, a newspaperman who had just come to the Museum in order to get over a nervous breakdown. "I thought secretarial work there would be more soothing than reporting," he later told a friend. Mr. Monaco, who was born in 1901 and retired in 1967, spent his thirty-one Museum years in the Department of Vertebrate Paleontology. He started out as secretary to Barnum Brown, the stellar collector of dinosaur bones, and subsequently served in a similar capacity to Walter Granger, George Gaylord Simpson, a noted fossil mammalogist on the Museum staff for three decades, and Edwin H. Colbert, now a curator in the department. Mr. Monaco's title was Technical Secretary to the Department of Vertebrate Paleontology, but he liked to refer to himself as the Prince of Monaco. One of his chores was to answer technical letters *with* technical letters. "Dr. Brown hired me as his secretary and then went away for three months," he once told an interviewer. "I spent this time going through hundreds of Museum letters so as to familiarize myself with key scientific words, which I wrote down, and indexed alphabetically, in a notebook." He handed his visitor a dilapidated black notebook whose entries ranged from "acetabulun" to "zygapophysis," and said, "When Dr. Brown came back, the first sentence he dictated to me was 'Dear Dr. Smith: The latest exploration in the field of stratigraphy has proven of such paleontological and geological significance that it has changed the existing conception of the Tertiary era.' I got it right, and I knew I was in. Have a cigar."

The two men lit up, and the Prince remarked that he was a passionate deep-sea fisherman and a longtime member of the Varuna Boat Club of Sheepshead Bay. "When I came to the Museum," he continued, "I'd go fishing every weekend in Sheepshead Bay or along the Jersey coast, either in my own boat or in one of the big cruisers of one of the rich club members. Mondays, I'd bring in my catch, and Albert Thomson, who had been an expedition cook for Dr. Andrews in the Gobi, or Charles

Lang, a preparator who was head of the vertebrate paleontology laboratory, would cook it. During severe winter
weather, when I didn't go out, I'd buy things from the
boats that *did*. Roy Andrews came to the lunches regu-
larly, and so did Walter Granger and George Simpson.
We'd have clams—little-necks, cherrystones, and steamers
—and cod, sea bass, flounder, fluke, scallops, striped bass,
snappers, and swordfish. I once made a list of everything
we'd had. It came to thirty-five different kinds of seafood.
On special occasions, when we entertained visiting scientists, we'd serve wine, in paper cups. The Museum was
a convivial place in those days. It was a great place for
romance. A countess, or so she said, armed with a sub-
poena, or so she said, once came shrieking down the cor-
ridors after one of the curators. I managed to hide him
in a back room and get her out of the building. Secretaries
would be found—" The rest of the conversation was off
the record.

After five or six years of seafood repasts, Dr. *Andrews*
was bumped, and the lunches wound up. The instrument
of the fourth director's downfall was a document known
in the Museum as the Ruthven Report. In 1941, when he
issued this report, "A Study of The American Museum of
Natural History made for the Board of Trustees," Alexander G. Ruthven was president of the University of
Michigan. Originally a herpetologist, he had composed
several previous reports, bearing titles like "Butler's Garter Snake," "Variations and Genetic Relationships of the
Garter Snakes" (including Butler's), and "Description of
a New Salamander from Iowa." (He came from Iowa
himself.) The trustees had invited him to study their in-

stitution at a time when its physical plant was deteriorating badly; when there was a large operating deficit; when Robert Moses, the Commissioner of Parks and an ex-officio trustee who held the City's purse strings as far as the Museum was concerned, was lambasting the place for "nepotism" on the board (which was graced by a number of second- or third-generation Dodges, Morgans, Osborns, Rockefellers, Whitneys, Warburgs, and Davisons); when three staff giants—Frank Chapman, Barnum Brown, and Clark Wissler—were about to retire; when a good many of the younger men were away on war service; and when office morale and scientific publication were at a low ebb.

"All is not well with this institution," Dr. Ruthven reported, and went on, in part:

> The building is poorly designed for museum purposes, and the best judgment has not been used in assigning space. . . . Thought should be given to bringing together the research rooms and materials. . . . One of the most serious situations is the result of the installation of large, expensive, and so-called "permanent" exhibits. . . . It will be enough to cite here the collection of woods and the anthropological hall. . . . Here one is completely overwhelmed with a tremendous series of almost identical flint points, baskets, ceramics, textiles, etc., and is wholly incapable of comprehending the details of any single object or group of objects. The same is true of the natural history displays. . . . [In the habitat groups] such details as food habits, enemies, breeding habits, and the like have been largely sacrificed to artistry. . . . It would have been better if long ago the Museum had begun to spend less time in the expansion of its exhibits and instead had undertaken the rearrangement and modernization of the older displays. . . . The older concept of large, elaborate, and ex-

pensive installations . . . should be replaced by a plan for
smaller, mobile units. . . . A weak administrative policy has
resulted in a faulty organization. . . . The principal difficulty,
then, being in administration, it is firmly believed that, if this
were strengthened . . . by changes in personnel . . . confidence would be restored. . . .

The chief change in personnel that resulted from the
Ruthven Report was the replacement of Dr. Andrews by
Dr. Albert E. Parr, a Norwegian-born ichthyologist who
came to the New York Aquarium in his twenties and was
professor of oceanography and director of the Peabody
Museum at Yale at the time he received the American
Museum's nod. According to some students of the Museum, the importation of Dr. Parr from New Haven was
a kind of Yale plot. President Davison, Yale 1918 and a
member of the Yale Corporation, was involved in it, and
so was Dr. Leonard C. Sanford, Yale 1890, an ornitho-
logically minded Museum trustee who in 1932 had negotiated with Lord Rothschild for the sale of the famous
Tring Collection of two hundred and eighty thousand
bird skins to the Museum, and, at the same time, had
persuaded Mrs. Harry Payne Whitney to put up the money
for it (two hundred and fifty thousand dollars)—but who
was less well disposed toward the Museum's Anthropology Department, anent which he once said, "Pisspottery
is not part of natural history." "Sanford was a tribal Eli,"
Dr. Murphy has said. "The choice of Dr. Parr was a Yale
conspiracy. There was an Eli group there that wanted him,
and an Eli group at New Haven that wanted to get rid of
him. Those old Elis were like Tammany. While they
were considering Dr. Parr for the Museum, Trubee asked

my opinion of a paper Parr had written. Trubee said he couldn't understand it. I wrote him that it was O.K., but incomprehensibly written. I ended my letter, 'For God's sake, don't let him write the labels here.'"

Dr. Parr may or may not have written labels for the Museum, but he did write some of the most mysterious annual reports of any director in the institution's history. In 1944, under the heading, "Times and the Museum: Through the Past Towards the Future," he touched on the Jesup Woods in this wise:

The vigor of a scientific and educational institution depends upon the extent to which it aligns itself with national traditions and seeks its intellectual nourishment in the experiences of the nation it serves. . . . [An] outstanding difference between American and European national experiences with the natural environment was that which developed from the influence of virgin forests upon human affairs. In Europe this influence culminated in the Middle Ages. The vast forests of medieval and pre-medieval Europe did not only dictate the physical, social, and economic ways of life of their inhabitants, but have also been credited with a profound influence upon their habits of thought, their mythology, and their emotional life. There is no isolation so complete, so crushing, or so inspiring as that of an inhabited clearing in the uncharted vastness of primeval woods.

In Europe, however, this stage had already been left far behind long before the nineteenth century. The relationship between forests and land under cultivation had reached a fairly stable and final pattern, with no urgent problems to impress themselves very strongly upon the minds of the people. Forestry therefore received only scant or no attention in European museums generally.

Not so in America. In so far as their relations to the forests were concerned the American people had been forced to telescope into less than two centuries a development which had taken several thousand years in Europe. . . . The forests were the greatest obstacles which they themselves or their nearest ancestors had had to overcome in wresting a foothold for themselves and their families in by far the largest part of the regions in which the nation had then become established. The forests were also an apparently unlimited source of wealth. Many could also recall having lived off the game of the woods, and many still did. The grandeur of virgin timber was still in vivid memory.

In his sponsorship of the Museum's great collection of American woods President Jesup thus . . . acted in ideal accord with the genuine interests of the nation. . . .

What an approach to the Western Union Telegraph Company's woodpecker-pecked telegraph pole, not to mention the Charter Oak! And what a switch from Roy Chapman Andrews' annual reports, one of which started out:

> A few months ago a lady who was a constant visitor of the Museum, came to my office to protest. She said that whenever she wanted to go into an exhibition hall it seemed as though it was always closed for renovation and she asked why we must continually have changes going on in the halls.
>
> I replied, "Instead of complaining about such a condition, you ought to be much pleased. It indicates, at least, that we are not satisfied with existing halls and are trying to keep them up to date. . . ."
>
> She replied, "I never thought of that. I guess you are right, after all."

As a showman, Dr. Parr had some original ideas; he was especially fond of the use of a color which his colleagues called a fire-engine red. "It has been an old tradition of natural history museums to attempt to match the color of dirty fingermarks in their general decor, and to seek a 'natural' color for the background of the objects they display," one of his early director's reports observed, and continued:

> . . . Probably the true explanation of this predilection for drab buffs and oatmeal grays lies in the meaning of the word "neutral," which is used in their description. Their "neutrality" consists chiefly in their inability to provoke any strong objections from anyone, although they may add to the boredom of all. . . . The remodeling of the Hall of Mexican and Central American Archaeology was the first occasion on which the American Museum broke with the tradition of color neutrality on a large scale, both within and around the exhibits. A further step in the same direction was taken when a strong red color, boldly complementary to the prevailing green in the habitat groups, was used in the redecoration of the Whitney Hall of Oceanic Birds, in order to stimulate interest and help bring out the beauty of the exhibits by a deliberate use of contrast rather than harmonious uniformity. . . .

"The red side walls which I introduced in the Hall of Pacific Bird Life pepped the whole thing up," says Dr. Parr. "They complemented the blue sky overhead. After I'd painted the Whitney Hall red, Dr. Sanford marched in, ready for the worst, and said, 'Damn it! I like it!' I started the Design Department at the Museum. We'd had a Preparation Department, but no designers. We were the first museum to have a design unit. I got Robert C. Osborn, the artist, to do cartoons for the cafeteria, but humor was too much for the trustees, and the drawings were eventually removed. Why should we be so serious? Why should education be so long-faced all the time? I had an idea of tucking in jokes throughout the Museum."

The opening of new exhibition halls—among them, the Hall of North American Forests and the Hall of the Biology of Man—flourished during Dr. Parr's regime, and he was largely responsible for the raising of curatorial salaries to the plateau of first-rank university professors. "Most salaries were behind college salaries," he says. "There was no policy about the advancement of scientific personnel. Some men got more than their opposite numbers. I got the board to adopt career schedules. Instead of advancement being a matter of chance or catching someone's eye, it became a matter of regular review." But the frustrated joker was not the soul of tact, and he failed to ingratiate himself with many of his trustees and scientific colleagues, two of whose exemplars—George Gaylord Simpson, the vertebrate paleontologist, and Ernst Mayr, the ornithologist—departed (for Harvard) during his administration. *His* departure as director was gracefully arranged (the Museum's bumping techniques have improved in its old age), and gracefully described by President White in the 1958–59 *Annual Report*:

An action of major importance was taken by the Board of Trustees during the past year with the adoption of a new administrative policy under the terms of which the Director of the Museum may return to full-time research, without sacrifice of income, after fifteen years of administrative service or upon reaching the age of 60. In adopting this policy the Trustees of the American Museum have attempted to offer one practicable solution to a problem that has not only affected this Museum but is also being pondered today in many similar organizations. The problem is to strike a balance between the operational pressures that confront a scholar-administrator and the yearning of the scholar to devote at least a part of his time to his particular academic or scientific studies.

Our belief is that the step we have taken offers a workable solution, for it means that from this time on a director of the American Museum may look forward to active years, after serving in an executive capacity, in which to follow the research or educational pursuits that had been curtailed during the term of his executive office.

Dr. Albert E. Parr . . . becomes the first person to benefit from this policy. On September 15, 1959, he will assume the post of Senior Scientist. On that date, the new director will take office. . . .

The Museum's first senior scientist until recently retained a big office on the fifth floor. He is now director emeritus and has gone back to New Haven to live. He writes articles for *Curator*, a scholarly quarterly published by the Museum, and other scientific periodicals. In these, he now touches less on fishes than on design and architecture. His style has loosened up. "It should be just as natural to enter a museum as it is to enter a store, a bank, or a bakery," he wrote recently, and went on:

Nevertheless, I venture the opinion that . . . the plaza and ground floor of almost any of the attractively designed new commercial buildings on Manhattan Island would offer a more inviting approach and entrance to a museum than any museum in New York can boast of presenting today. . . . We must demand of the museum architecture of the future that it reverse this relationship, or, at least, remove our handicap. Our appearance should be gay without being frivolous, informal without being inelegant, and seductive without being undignified.

Among the many forbidding aspects of traditional museum architecture is the prevalence of exterior stairways for the visitor to climb before he can reach the august sanctuary of

his destination. These status symbols of devotion to the higher
things in life would seem to have gained special and unusual
currency among the designers of museums until quite recent
times. . . . When I express myself somewhat unenthusiastically
about the merits of currently modern museum buildings, I
wish to make it perfectly clear that I have the greatest
esteem both for the esthetic qualities and for the functional
advantages of many of the edifices I have specifically in
mind, and that I would not presume to criticize their architecture any more than I would criticize the beauty of Mont
Blanc. I merely wish to suggest that the top of Mont Blanc
is no place for museum exhibits.

7

HISTORIANS SHOULD probably not jump around so much, chronologically, but have we taken proper leave of Henry Fairfield Osborn? He himself did not take leave of the Museum when he retired as president at the end of 1932. Still an active trustee, chairman of the board's Committee on Buildings and Plans, and Honorary Curator-in-Chief of the Department of Vertebrate Paleontology, he continued to keep an office in the Tower Room at the east end of the fifth floor of the Romanesque Revival wing. There, assisted by a detail of secretaries—he had, at various times, up to five ladies serving in this capacity—and a group of fossil-oriented colleagues, he kept revising the proofs of his Proboscidea monograph, and, on occasion, listened sympathetically to the complaints of staff members who were unable to get President Davison to do just what they wanted him to do. Osborn died, at seventy-eight, at Castle Rock, his ancestral country place at Garrison on Hudson. This, which is still owned by members of his family, includes a castle, as well as a woodsy lodge, where, for the better part of the year (April till December) in the 1920s and early 1930s, the president (and subsequent honorary president) would attend to his correspondence and other Museum matters. His secretaries took turns going up there two or three days a week. "We'd take a train—two of us, generally—from One Hundred and Twenty-fifth Street at six-thirty in the morning and go back in the late afternoon," one of them has said. "Sometimes there'd be nothing to do except bring the mail. As long as Mrs. Osborn was alive, we were not asked to the main house for lunch. Servants would bring us cold lamb sandwiches at the lodge. The lodge itself, on the top of a mountain, was pretty cold sometimes. We were sort of handmaidens."

Professor Osborn's last decade was saddened by the death of his wife, who idolized him and predeceased him by five years; embittered by the failure to materialize of one of his favorite projects, an Inter-Museum Promenade across Central Park, between The American Museum and the Metropolitan Museum of Art, which he tried hard to promote in negotiations with the City of New York for a dozen or more years; and clouded (in the eyes of some) by an enthusiastic trip he made in 1934 to Nazi Germany, where he picked up an honorary degree at the Johann Wolfgang Goethe University. Some of Osborn's friends have ascribed this enthusiasm to the vagaries of old age, but as early as 1916 the professor had contributed an approving preface to his fellow trustee Madison Grant's

The Passing of the Great Race, or, the Racial Basis of European History, in which Mr. Grant had written:

As a result of certain religious and social doctrines, now happily becoming obsolete, race consciousness has been greatly impaired among civilized nations. . . . In the city of New York and elsewhere in the United States there is a native American aristocracy resting upon layer after layer of immigrants of lower races. . . . From a material point of view slaves are often more fortunate than freemen when treated with reasonable humanity and when their elemental wants of food, clothing and shelter are supplied. . . . There exists today a widespread and fatuous belief in the power of environment, as well as of education and opportunity to alter heredity, which arises from the dogma of the brotherhood of man. . . . Thus the view that the Negro slave was an unfortunate cousin of the white man . . . played no small part with the sentimentalists of the Civil War period and it has taken us fifty years to learn that speaking English, wearing good clothes and going to school and to church does not transform a Negro into a white man. . . . Americans will have a similar experience with the Polish Jew, whose dwarf stature, peculiar mentality and ruthless concentration on self-interest are being engrafted upon the stock of the nation. . . . Whether we like to admit it or not, the result of the mixture of two races, in the long run, gives us a race reverting to the more ancient, generalized and lower type. The cross between a white man and an Indian is an Indian; the cross between a white man and a Negro is a Negro; the cross between a white man and a Hindu is a Hindu; and the cross between any of the three European races and a Jew is a Jew. . . . Among marksmen, it has been noted that nearly all the great rifle-shots in England or America have had light colored eyes. . . . The Nordic race is nearly everywhere distinguished by great stature. . . . No one can question the race value of stature who observes on the streets of London the contrast between the Piccadilly gentleman of Nordic race and the cockney costermonger of the old Neolithic type. . . . Indiscriminate efforts to preserve babies among the lower classes often result in serious injury to the race. . . . When it becomes thoroughly understood that the children of mixed marriages between contrasted races belong to the lower type, the importance of transmitting in unimpaired purity the blood inheritance of ages will be appreciated at its full value, and to bring half-breeds into the world will be regarded as a social and racial crime of the first magnitude. The laws against miscegenation must be greatly extended if the higher races are to be maintained.

. . . A record of the desperate efforts of the conqueror classes in India to preserve the purity of their blood persists until this very day in their carefully regulated system of castes. In our Southern States Jim Crow cars and social discriminations have exactly the same purpose and justification. . . . Negroes have demonstrated throughout recorded time that they are a stationary species and that they do not possess the potentiality of progress or initiative from within. . . . We Americans must realize that the altruistic ideals which have controlled our social development during the past century and the maudlin sentimentalism that has made America "an asylum for the oppressed" are sweeping the nation toward a racial abyss. . . .

Osborn's sympathy with Grant's racial theories—in a *second* preface, to a 1917 edition of *The Passing*, the professor wrote: "It should be remembered . . . that many of the dark-haired, dark-eyed youths of Plattsburg and other volunteer training camps are often three-fourths or seven-eights Nordic, because it only requires a single dark-eyed ancestor to lend the dark hair and eye color to an otherwise pure Nordic strain"—caused Dr. Robert H. Lowie, an American-Indian-specializing ethnologist who had left the Museum in 1921 after thirteen years there, to decline to sign the Osborn seventieth-birthday tribute, for reasons less personal than Dr. Bumpus'. "I am not a friend or admirer of President Osborn's. Specifically, his sponsorship of Mr. Grant's book, in my judgment, puts him beyond the pale as a representative of science," he wrote Dr. William K. Gregory, a multiple-department Museum scientist (Ichthyology, Comparative and Human Anatomy, Physical Anthropology), who, as secretary of the Committee for the Celebration of Professor Osborn's Seventieth Birthday, had sounded him out.

Dr. Gregory, an early Osborn research assistant who had his ups and downs with his chief but whose general stance is indicated by the fact that the professor inscribed copies of three of his books to Gregory as his "fidus Achates," took polite exception to this judgment. "The over-conciseness of my previous communication has not made for clarity," Dr. Lowie replied, and went on, in part:

> To President Osborn I have never imputed Mr. Grant's sadism. However, his active sponsorship of the book, as attested by his two prefaces, proves to my mind that he substantially shares his friend's prejudices and condones even his counterfeiting of biological laws. . . . I admit that his conduct, inexcusable as I consider it, does not automatically exclude constructive work. But I regard the offender as "beyond the pale" *as a spokesman and interpreter of the scientific spirit.* . . . I personally find it impossible to render homage to President Osborn. . . . The issues are important moral ones, I think. . . .

Twenty-three years later—in 1950—Dr. Murphy, in a generally friendly article in the *Scientific Monthly*, "Reminiscences of Professor Osborn," wrote: "Few would deny . . . that he had been led somewhat astray in his views on superior and inferior 'racial' categories of modern Caucasian man."

On the more cheery side, the fourth president's last

few years were brightened by the frequent presence at the Museum of Meshie, a girl chimpanzee from West Africa that Dr. Henry C. Raven, a staff anatomist, acquired in 1929 in the French Cameroons as an orphaned baby. (Her mother had been shot when the daughter was captured.) Dr. Raven installed Meshie in his Long Island home, where he and his wife reared her with their children. At four, Meshie could handle a fork and spoon as well as a child of her age; she drank milk out of a thermos bottle, after pouring it herself; she could untie knots with her teeth. Dr. Raven got into the habit of bringing her to the Museum, where she rode the long fifth-floor corridor in a kiddie car. Professor Osborn would summon her to his office when distinguished visitors or the children or grandchildren of friends were calling on him. President Davison continued this practice—he had Meshie to lunch with Edna Ferber and the Ralph Pulitzers, among others. One of these high-level visits has been described by Dr. Raven:

Took Meshie to see some friends of Mr. Trubee Davison's. They were sitting quietly in the inner office when Meshie rode in on her kiddie car. There was a boy of four and a girl of three sitting on a table beside their mother. Meshie climbed on the table beside the children. The little girl at first shrank away from Meshie but was reassured by her mother and Meshie put her arm about the child without at first touching her. When the child was no longer afraid, Meshie looked out the window at people on the street. Later she sat on the floor and turned the leaves of a telephone book with the little boy sitting beside her. It was then that the little girl of her own initiative got down beside Meshie, and, leaning over so her face was close to Meshie's, said, in her childish voice, "Meshie, can I ride your kiddie car?"

The Museum had a staff dining room in those days, with tablecloths, waitresses, and a good forty-five-cent lunch (the room was later supplanted by the present concessionaired employees' cafeteria), and Meshie, riding in from the elevator on her kiddie car, lunched there off and on, seated in a baby's high chair, for several years. In 1934, when she was three feet tall, weighed seventy pounds, and was getting sulky, Dr. Raven sold her to the Brookfield Zoo in Chicago. "Harry went out there on a visit," Dr. Shapiro has said, "and asked to call on her in her cage. She was very powerful, and given to fits of violence, and he was warned not to, but he went in and she threw herself on him, overcome with joy. She had recognized him after a year. Chimpanzees aren't supposed to remember this long." In 1937, she died, after giving birth to a daughter. She was sent back to the Museum, where, mounted, sitting hunched on a log in a glass case, gazing out with one hand cupped under her chin, she is now on display, anonymously, in the Hall of Primates.

As an anatomist, Dr. Raven, whose published papers include one "On the anatomy and evolution of the locomotor apparatus of the nipple-tailed ocean sunfish (*Masturus lanceolatus*)," was sometimes led into less happy extracurricular bypaths. In 1940 and 1941, testifying before the Grand Jury and for the Bronx District Attorney's Office in the trial of a janitor for the murder of a ten-year-old girl, he identified—after sixty hours of study—nine out of one hundred and thirty-three charred fragments of bones found in the furnace ashes of the janitor's cellar as those of a young human being. His testimony contributed materially to the verdict, which sent the accused to the electric chair.

Matters of life and death have risen more directly in the Museum's orbit. In 1926, Dr. G. Kingsley Noble, who had taken charge of the Department of Herpetology almost at its inception, looked into a much-discussed experiment of Paul Kammerer, a Viennese zoologist.

> . . . The . . . experiment was done with the midwife toad [the late Richard B. Goldschmidt, a University of California professor, has written], the male of which seizes the egg strings laid by the female, winds them around his hind legs, and carries them about until hatching time. An exception to the rule, this male was devoid of the thick pigmented thumb pads which other frog and toad males need for the standard type of copulation. Kammerer claimed that he could change the mating habits of the midwife toad to those of ordinary toads by breeding them under conditions used for other toads. Such males not only stopped "midwifery" but also developed the thumb pad and, again, this new induced character was said to be inherited . . . if crossed to the original form.
>
> In the discussion of these claims, statements were found in Kammerer's papers which did not tally. . . . The explosion came when an American visitor, Noble, looked at the specimens exhibited in Kammerer's institute and found that the "induced" dark thumb pad was injected with India ink. . . . Soon after this Kammerer . . . committed suicide.

Dr. Noble, who was more interested in psychology than in systematics, went on to develop at the Museum a Department of Experimental Biology, which at first studied the effects of hormones on frogs and lizards, and later expanded into the present cat-rat-bird-and-so-forth Department of Animal Behavior. He himself died at forty-six, in 1940; according to some, the Kammerer tragedy killed him. He was probably the Museum's greatest loss by early death.

I want to get on, or back, to Mr. Davison, so let us take leave of Professor Osborn with a few quotations about him, culled from a cornucopia I have filled:

Walter Meister, the Jesup-toe-owning controller: "Professor Osborn never picked up the telephone to make an interoffice communication. He generally dictated letters, on presidential stationery, to members of the staff, and he sometimes sent them telegrams, which slowed things up. His letters were delivered by hand. He wouldn't carry anything himself, not even an envelope. He had two offices —one presidential, one paleontological. If he wanted a memorandum taken from his fifth-floor office to his second-floor office, one of his secretaries would call a messenger; the two men—Osborn and the messenger—might go down in the same elevator."

Cleveland E. Dodge, a third-generation trustee, now honorary: "His sister-in-law, Mrs. William Church Osborn, was my aunt. He ran the Museum on a personal basis. He appointed special committees of trustees to concern themselves with different departments. At one time, for example, Childs Frick and Junius Morgan were on the Vertebrate Paleontology Committee, Kermit Roosevelt and Madison Grant on Mammals of the World, William K. Vanderbilt and James H. Perkins (president of the Farmers' Loan & Trust Co.) on Fishes, Hamilton Rice and I on Geology and Geography, and so on. This was cut out under President White. Until the Depression, J. P. Morgan, Ogden Mills, my father, and others would make up the annual deficit. Professor Osborn couldn't under-

stand why this didn't continue *after* the Depression set in.
Before the Depression, the wealthy trustees would give
the annual dinners at their houses. White-tie. Now these
dinners are held at the Museum. Black-tie. Osborn was
a very nice man. He had a very gracious personality. He
liked to have his own way. He got a lot of these wealthy
men on the board. They were a very loyal bunch. (One
of the wealthy men whom Osborn welcomed to the board
—in his first year as president—was the junior J. P. Morgan, whose affection for the Museum was such that he
once wrote the professor, "I indeed wish with you that
we could change jobs for a little while. The peace of the
Museum, although it is the peace of poverty, would, I am
sure, do me good. . . .") He ran a wonderful institution,
with a lot of money from bequests and a nice balance on
the board of businessmen and people interested in scientific
things. We've always had a very strong investment committee; it used to meet at Brown Brothers and it now
meets at Brown Brothers Harriman. Mrs. Osborn was a
great help to her husband. She talked the Museum up to
everybody."

A lady curator, now emeritus, who has worked at the
Museum for many years: "He was impossible. He was exceedingly rude. He'd almost knock you over getting into
the elevator."

Dr. Harry L. Shapiro: "I was twenty-four when I
came here in the summer of 1926. I was in my last Ph.D.
year at Harvard and tutoring undergraduates when Earnest Hooton, one of my professors, recommended me for
an opening in the Museum's anthropology department.
I rearranged my schedule for a couple of days around

Christmas of 1925 and came down for an interview. Dr. Wissler, the chairman of the department, was off on a field trip, so I saw Dr. Pliny E. Goddard, the acting chairman. After our talk, he said, 'The Professor wants to see you.' Osborn took me to lunch, and then invited me to his house for dinner. I bowed out. I'd been down two days, and I wanted to go back. Dr. Goddard was horrified. It was most unusual for the president to interview on such a lowly level, he said, not to mention *lunch*. Not to mention *dinner!* Back in Cambridge, I was bawled out by Hooton. Well, I was appointed, and the job was held for me until July. The whole Museum was an extension of Osborn. During my first winter here, he'd often walk down the corridor and drop in on me. He was Hudson River Bracketed in a way. He had a very lordly manner. He had a squirearchical attitude. He had a belief in himself that you rarely encounter these days. I was enchanted with his method of correcting his books in page proof. He couldn't be bothered to correct galleys. This system was a little expensive. He used to get staff members to help him with his books. 'I want a section on thus-and-so,' he would say. Poor Nelson wrote most of his *Men of the Stone Age*."

Poor Nelson was Nels C. Nelson, who joined the Museum in 1912 and died in 1964, at eighty-nine, as Curator Emeritus of Prehistoric Archeology. He was a resourceful field man. On one occasion, as Roy Chapman Andrews' archeologist on the 1925 Central Asiatic expedition, he got into a situation where it looked as though some Mongol nomads were going to make trouble. Nelson pretended to be a magician. He had a glass eye, which he used as a prop. In the folklore of the Museum, there are two versions of his trick. (1) He took the eye out, and replaced it in its socket. The terrified natives ran away. (2) He took the eye out, placed it on a rock, and said, "I'm keeping an eye on you." The terrified natives ran away.

Dr. Margaret Mead, one of the lights on Dr. Shapiro's staff, who has been associated with the Museum since 1926: "Osborn *ran* the Museum. Since then, the president has been . . . well, *normal*. The last days of Osborn were very capricious. He was powerful and capricious. Salaries were thousands of dollars apart because of his capriciousness. Osborn was a magnificent old devil. This was his dream, and he built it. He was arbitrary and opinionated, but I got my first view of many things from his books and the exhibits he sponsored. Like Thomas Jefferson, he was a wealthy man who was also a scientific explorer. He certainly was the Establishment with a capital E. We would never have had the Museum without him. He was the kind of scientist who gathers around him specialists."

Dr. Robert Cushman Murphy, in his "Reminiscences":

> If . . . Professor Osborn did not always welcome opinions that differed from his own in the administrative sphere, I should hasten to make it clear that in scientific research no such attitude was ever apparent. Here he not only tolerated but actively encouraged criticism of his own interpretations and conclusions. He never . . . expressed either objection or pique when even his youngest fellow-workers disagreed with him on public platforms. . . . The Professor was a man of such unvarying dignity and serene self-confidence that merriment could hardly be called a feature of his daily life as seen by his colleagues. . . . Nevertheless . . . he could be wholly jovial during hours of relaxation with the members of his family, particularly with those of the youngest genera-

tion. [Osborn was the great-grandfather of some of Dr. Murphy's grandchildren.] . . . He carried many profound discoveries of a scientific epoch into homes and schools throughout the world, changing "dinosaur" from a high-brow to a household word and making Mesozoic dragons almost as familiar to children as the creatures of Noah's Ark. . . .

"Osborn followed some of Madison Grant's prejudices," Dr. Murphy has said in private conversation, "but he was evasive about them. He wouldn't see the press when they sent Jewish reporters to question him on some of his published statements. He delegated this to Dr. Gregory. He did a lot of sound paleontological work, but when he got into generalities he went astray. Kingsley Noble knocked some of his tritubercular-teeth theories into a cocked hat. Osborn liked to use quasi-philosophical terms, and this sometimes led him into an almost mystical sphere."

George Gaylord Simpson, in the Dictionary of American Biography:

Participating in the reaction against Victorian mechanistic determinism, Osborn developed a theory of vitalistic determinism personal to him and acceptable to few either in the old schools or the new. He rejected any important random influences in evolution and held that mutation is a mere accident interfering with, not determining, the direction of evolution, a belief based in part on a misunderstanding of the implications and nature of mutations. . . . [Some of his doctrines] appeared mystical or quasi-religious and not scientific to many of his contemporaries, and they were made further unpalatable by their expression in a complex terminology peculiar to Osborn. . . . On the other hand many of the descriptive principles first or best expressed by Osborn, such as that of adaptive radiation, became in his lifetime fundamental in evolutionary theory. . . . In his attempts to synthesize

experimental and observational data Osborn was definitely
ahead of his contemporaries. . . . He often invited criticism
and advice but rarely acted on it. . . . He considered any
hints of difficulty or impossibility as inadmissibly destructive
criticisms. This characteristic sometimes invited failure and
resentment, but it also sometimes resulted in accomplishing
the apparently impossible. . . .

And, in the Museum's 1935 *Annual Report:*

. . . He was the sponsor and father of the Department of
Vertebrate Paleontology, which is now without a peer.

Professor Osborn, or his ghost, still awaits a full-length
biography. The Osborn family once invited Dr. Simpson
to write one, but when he agreed, on the condition that no
strings were to be attached, the family *wouldn't* agree.

8

A S AN AMERICAN MUSEUM PRESIDENT, Professor Osborn was a sport. He is the only scientist ever to have headed Morris K. Jesup's innocent attraction. All the other presidents have been businessmen. Osborn liked to think of himself as an honorary businessman. In 1926, making the best of all possible worlds (can one *ever* take leave of this protean man?), he posted copies of the *Annual Report* to members of the New York State Chamber of Commerce. He had these wrapped up in a special transparent cover, on which he wrote, "As a grandson of one of the former presidents of the Chamber of Commerce (Jonathan Sturges, his mother's father) and son of one of the presidents of the Illinois Central Railroad, the President of the American Museum of Natural History desires to call attention especially to the present and future influence of the American Museum on the trade and commerce of the United States." "Our expeditions, explorations, and collections now cover the following countries," he continued, and proceeded to list forty-three geographical areas, including "The Atlantic and Pacific Oceans," "The Indian Ocean," and "The Himalaya Mountains." His wrapper copy wound up, "Will not every Member of the Chamber of Commerce lend his influence and example by adding to the Endowment Fund of The American Museum of Natural History in any amount in order to push this great work along and spread American civilization, American commerce, and American influence throughout the world." No question mark.

His successor, Trubee Davison, was, at the time of his election, a director of the New York Trust Company and the Mutual Life Insurance Company. (*His* successor, Mr. White, is a partner in the banking firm of White, Weld & Co. and a director of the American Cyanamid Company.) An easygoing Republican who liked to describe himself as "the first member of Hoover's Cabinet to be put in a museum," Mr. Davison made this transition in 1933, when Life Member Franklin D. Roosevelt became President (of the U.S.). Before being appointed Assistant Secretary of War for Air, Davison had been a New York Assemblyman from Nassau County, Long Island. He had been at the helm of the Museum only a year when he accepted a position as Robert Moses' manager in this ex-officio trustee's unsuccessful gubernatorial campaign against Herbert Lehman. Davison's political activities caused some Museum hands to feel that he simply wanted to take a breather on Central Park West before springing again to public service, but this *reculer-pour-mieux-sauter* theory (which cannot be evaluated precisely, in view of the long Republican eclipse that set in) has received no support from its subject. "My father had been on the Museum board, and its treasurer," he told a man who recently interviewed him at his place in Locust Valley. "In 1922, when he died, I succeeded him as a trustee. Ten years later, when Professor Osborn was planning to retire, a trustees' committee of Junius Morgan, Childs Frick, and Cleveland E. Dodge asked me to take the Museum on, as president. It was the one thing in the world I wanted to do most."

One of the first things the new president did was to spend three and a half months in Africa, with his wife, shooting and taking photographs of elephants. "Four of the eight elephants in Akeley Hall are ours," he said. "On my return, in the fall of 1933, my brother Harry met me at Quarantine and said that Charles Hayden, the investment banker, was interested in the Planetarium. The Reconstruction Finance Corporation had agreed to put up the money for a building—it eventually came to eight hundred thousand dollars—but one hundred and fifty thousand dollars more was needed for the instruments and apparatus: a Zeiss projector and a Copernican orrery. The government couldn't pay for these, since they were manufactured in Germany, and it had to buy everything here. Well, the next day Kermit Roosevelt, one of our trustees, got on the phone and told me the same thing about Charlie Hayden. I didn't know him, but I went down to see him at the Hayden, Stone office. He was a short fellow, sitting in a revolving chair. He revolved around so that I was facing his back. 'The greatest spiritual thing in my life has been the Adler Planetarium in Chicago,' he said. 'You're all set on the building, but I'm sorry that you have to use Museum funds for the instrument. I'll give ten thousand dollars if you get fourteen others to put up the rest.' I went to the trustees and said, 'I think if we name the Planetarium after him, he'll give the whole hundred and fifty thousand.' They agreed, provisionally, to try this. So I went down again and put the proposition. 'I'll be very glad to do it,' he said. I offered to show him plans, but he said not to bother. I was in his office only five minutes. When the Planetarium opened in 1935, he gave a big dinner, at which Bob Moses, in the course of a speech, congratulated him on having bought immortality so cheaply. We should have asked him for a million dollars."

Another important newcomer to make itself felt on the Museum campus in the early Davison presidential period was the Rothschild bird collection. Although this had been acquired in Osborn's day, it was not completely unpacked, stored in study cabinets, and catalogued, until 1938. Lionel Walter Rothschild, the eldest son of the first English Rothschild peer, was a naturalist who built up on his father's estate at Tring the largest and most valuable collection of zoological specimens ever assembled by one man. In 1898, he had borrowed from the Museum two Galápagos turtles (one mounted, one skeleton, both the fruit of providential deaths in the Central Park Menagerie), which, despite several dunning letters from Professor J. A. Allen, he did not return until 1909. Such delays are not uncommon in the scientific world, and the Museum bore him no grudge. In 1927, Dr. Sanford, the tribal Eli and ornithological trustee, called, without appointment, at the Tring Museum. "It was my first visit there," he told a friend twenty years later. "I rang the

bell, and a German porter came out and said, 'It's Sunday. You can't come in.' I said I'd come all the way
from New York to see Dr. Ernest Hartert. He was the
director of Rothschild's museum. 'It's Sunday,' the porter
said. 'You can't come in.' 'If you tell me what day it is
again, I'll beat your brains out,' I said. Dr. Hartert stuck
his head out of a second-story window at this juncture.
'Are you the great Dr. Sanford?' he asked, and invited
me in." Four years later, when Dr. Hartert's employer
was hard up (he had worked in his father's bank as a
young man, but left it at thirty), he asked Dr. Sanford
whether the Museum would like to buy his birds. "He
had his choice of selling his insect collection or his bird
collection," Dr. Murphy has said. "He thought the birds
would fetch more. They fetched a little less than a dollar
a skin. After Dr. Sanford had persuaded Mrs. Whitney to
put up the two hundred and fifty thousand dollars that
was asked, he went to England for the final negotiations.
Our director, our lawyer, and I accompanied him. My
wife subsequently joined me, to help me and the Tring
staff get the specimens packed for shipping. It took us
four months to fill one hundred and eighty-five 30-by-30-
by-60-inch wooden cases. Mrs. Murphy prepared a genus
index of seven hundred and forty foolscap pages. After
we'd gotten the specimens sorted out here—some of the
series are irreplaceable—we gave the original type specimens of the British Isles to the British Museum. There
were thirteen, most of them subspecies. I think the Red
Grouse was the only full type. Dr. Sanford conveyed the
gift in person and presented it to the trustees of the British

Museum with the compliments of the American Museum."

Thanks largely to the Rothschild haul and the wide-ranging collecting activities of Dr. Chapman and Dr. Murphy, who once held the unique title of Curator of Oceanic Birds, the Museum is as unrivaled in birds as it is in dinosaurs. "Frank Chapman told me that our bird collections were so good that they were better than the rest of the world's put together," Mr. Davison went on, after his Planetarium reminiscence, and this reminded his Locust Valley visitor (to digress again) of a Chapman exercise in employee relations that turned out, over a period of forty-one years, to be something of a financial coup. In 1917, Mrs. Elsie M. B. Reichenberger, a part-time volunteer in the Bird Department, asked the management whether she might "receive some remuneration for my work at the Museum for the coming year." This suggestion was at first declined, but in January, 1918, Dr. Chapman went to bat with the director, Dr. Lucas, and got Mrs. R. $37.50 a month for her half-time services. In the fall of that year, he had her raised to a hundred dollars a month as a full-time assistant. A widow, she presently married Mr. Walter W. Naumburg, a banker, and continued to work at the Museum as a Research Associate (unpaid). Between 1926 and 1932, she financed ornithological field expeditions, mainly in Brazil, that brought in some thirteen thousand specimens, including a Rhea's egg from Paraguay. She predeceased her husband, and in 1959, when he died, the Museum's Frank M. Chapman Memorial Fund, which the Naumburgs had founded, received from her estate a slice of International Business Machines stock that now hovers, on the stock market, at an altitude of between one and a half million and two million dollars.

The Museum's fifth president took office at a time when even the institution's rich friends were relatively strapped. "Because of the Depression," Mr. Davison said, "our salaries were reduced, some of our positions were abolished, our great exploration program was suspended, and ten of our exhibition halls were closed, for part of the time, in rotation. The City reduced its allotment to us, and the trustees could no longer be counted on to make up the annual deficit. I decided to broaden the base on the financial end. We had to get small contributions because the big ones weren't there. I set up a Men's Committee and a Women's Committee to raise funds. That's how Alec White, a country neighbor of mine, came into the Museum picture —on the Men's Committee. I asked him to go on the board in 1947. As president, he handled the endowment brilliantly. When he took office in 1951, this fund was around sixteen million dollars; in 1967, it was over fifty-two million. Gifts and bequests have been added, of course."

President White had an alter ego in the person of Mr. Charles DeWolf Gibson, a retired vice president and director of the Air Reduction Company who became a Museum trustee in 1953 and was elected vice president in 1959. Working fulltime out of the president's office in an executive capacity, Mr. Gibson supervised Museum affairs, presided at the monthly meetings of the Management Board and at trustees meetings, led the Men and Women's Committees and all fund raising activities, and generally represented Mr. White in day to day activities at the Museum.

At the annual meeting of the trustees in October, 1968, Mr. Gibson retired as vice president, Mr. White was elected chairman of the board, and Mr. Gardner D. Stout of Dominick & Dominick was elected president.

Mr. Davison asked his visitor to stay for lunch, and the two men presently repaired to the dining room, where they were joined by Mrs. Davison and a small dog.

"I've taught him to bark when I say 'Robert Moses,'" the host said. "Moses tried to put up a bridge across the Sound from Rye to just off my place. Robert Moses!" Nothing happened.

"*Robert Moses!*" he repeated, and the dog jumped up on a window seat overlooking the Sound and barked.

"The Osborns were a little on the formal side," said Mrs. Davison, who is a daughter of Endicott Peabody. "They sent their boys to Groton. It was something of a strain when they visited my parents."

Mr. Davison coughed.

"We got some awfully good pictures of elephants in Africa," his wife said. "Our safari was very luxurious. We had to get up at four in the morning, but we had twenty-five natives to take care of us. Dr. Frederick Tilney, the brain surgeon—he was medical director of the New York Neurological Institute—asked us to bring back an elephant brain. We brought two. I don't think they proved anything. They were not in very good shape. Did you know that it takes three and a half days to skin an elephant? Trubee had a little trouble at the Museum after coming in as president. Professor Osborn continued to throw his weight around. Trubee made a point of never advising Alec White."

As president of the Museum, Mr. Davison exhibited a freewheeling attitude toward natural history not unlike that of the late Gilbert H. Grosvenor, president of the National Geographic Society, toward geography. "Our interpretation of geography is very wide," Dr. Grosvenor once told a man who had queried the relevance of the *National Geographic Magazine*'s coverage of such subjects as the tetrahedral principle in kite structure, American battle monuments in France, and the National Gallery of Art. "When I see a subject that I think would be interesting to our readers, I don't scrutinize it to see if it's geographic." Davison, an aviator in the First World War, is an old friend of Charles A. Lindbergh, and in 1934 he obtained for the Museum a Lindbergh plane, in which the colonel and his wife had flown around the world. This curious object of natural history was suspended in the Hall of Ocean Life, along with the Amagansett whale. "I thought the plane would be interesting to our public, and I think it *was*," its sponsor said to his guest, "but the Ruthven Report objected to it, so we sent it to the Air Force Museum."

The Reconstruction Finance Corporation bonds for the Planetarium defaulted, and in 1948, some time after Mr. Hayden's death, they were bought by the Museum, with the assistance of a $200,000 gift from a Hayden family foundation, and added to the Museum endowment. Interest on them is paid by something called The American Museum of Natural History Planetarium Authority. The Planetarium itself, which is administered by the Department of Astronomy, is doing nicely. Its annual attendance averages around six hundred thousand, and it is a valuable

come-on, since many of the people who come to see its
Sky Theatre go on to the rest of the Museum. It has a
staff of three professional astronomers, among them Dr.
Kenneth L. Franklin, a pioneer tuner-in to radio signals
from Jupiter, and a couple of astronomical educators, who
give courses in telescope using, basic star identification,
celestial navigation, and the like to young and old alike.
"Our emphasis on education is a legacy from Dr. Joseph
M. Chamberlain, who ran the Planetarium from 1956
until 1964 and was later an assistant director of the Museum," says Dr. Franklyn M. Branley, chairman of the
Planetarium and the author of more than fifty scientific
books for young people. Dr. Chamberlain's successor (both
as head of the Planetarium and as assistant director of the
Museum), Dr. Thomas D. Nicholson, a world authority
on nautical astronomy and master mariner, likes to point
out that the Planetarium has grown from a spectacle to an
educational force, with summer programs for high-school
students and evening courses for laymen. He also likes to
point out a sign, containing an arrow, on the first-floor
landing, which reads "Solar System and Rest Rooms." Dr.
Nicholson thinks the humor is unintentional, but Dr. Branley is not sure.

9

Dr. James A. Oliver, The American Museum's current director, is an old Missouri boy (born 1914) with a Ph.D. from the University of Michigan, where he specialized in herpetology. Friendly, convivial, hard-working, and energetic, he mixes easily with his staff, has a gift for anecdote, and likes to recite poetry in off hours. Snakes hit him early. "I can't remember a time when I wasn't interested in them," he says. "My family had a farm a hundred and twenty miles south of St. Louis, where I spent my first twenty-one Christmases and most of my summers. Wonderful snake country—copperheads, rattlesnakes, spreading adders. In town, I frequented the St. Louis Zoo and went on so many snake-hunting trips with the reptile curator that whenever I played hooky from school the principal would call the Zoo before he called my home."

The Museum's sixth scientific head was no stranger to its halls when he succeeded Dr. Parr in 1959. He had served as a curator of amphibians and reptiles under

Charles M. Bogert from 1942 to 1948, taking time off
for the Second World War, in which he was communications officer on a destroyer. Although the conflict came
between him and amphibians and reptiles, it did not cut
him off altogether. "We stood offshore at the Normandy
landings for eighteen days," he says, "bombarding and
offering screening covering for the landings, and then
were in on the invasion of southern France. We later did
convoy service. I was fortunate in being communications
officer, since I could go ashore everywhere to pick up the
latest instructions, and also snakes, frogs, chameleons, and
other lizards, which I sent to the Museum." In this way,
he collected herpetological specimens in Cuba, Panama,
Malta, North Africa, and Trinidad. In 1945 he went to
Okinawa, where he took in a supply of sea snakes, which
flourish only in the warm waters of the Pacific and Indian
Oceans. "The war was finished," he has said, "so we
could attract them with a light over the side of the ship.
Sea snakes are venomous but docile." On the way home
through the Pacific, he persuaded his superior officers to
let his destroyer drop out of the squadron for a while so
that he could chase sea turtles in a small boat. He got
three.

Oliver left the Museum's employ on his first time round
to become assistant professor of zoology at the University
of Florida. He left *there* after three years. "It was too
hot," he recalls, "and I missed the cultural stimulation."
Cool, stimulating, reptilian-amphibian years at the Bronx
Zoo followed. As its director in 1958 and part of 1959,
he continued to preside (as curator of the House of Reptiles, whose design and construction he directed) over a

group of five hundred pythons, anacondas, lizards, turtles,
alligators, crocodiles, and so on, whom he patted affection-
ately and treated, in air-conditioned comfort, to record-
ings of Chopin, Gounod, Offenbach, Rimski-Korsakov,
Bizet, Debussy, Ravel, Beethoven, and Rudolf Friml. (He
doesn't think that snakes like boogie-woogie.) His present
post involves the administration of six hundred employees,
budget talks with City officials, and policy discussions with
more than thirty trustees. Removed from active snakesman-
ship, Dr. Oliver is thought by some of his friends to miss
his old scaly contacts. He presides over a staff that includes, along with members already mentioned, an army
of dedicated specialists to whom one cannot hope to do
full individual justice. Let us reluctantly pass over, then,
Dr. Willis Gertsch, the arachnologist, who keeps forty
pet tarantulas in big glass jars in his office ("Tarantulas
are much maligned"); Dr. Bobb Schaeffer, chairman of
the Vertebrate Paleontology Department, curator of fossil
fishes, one of the country's three full-time paleoichthy-
ologists, and a man who wears smart striped shirts and
figured ties in the winter but sits on banks of shale, more
informally clad, in the summer, slitting the rock until he
finds something of interest, preferably a fossil fish ("I
have a nice Jurassic working area in northeast Wyoming");
Dr. Malcolm C. McKenna, the Frick Associate Curator,
who often spends *his* summers in the same general locale,
going through several hundred tons of sandstone for a
typical take of a hundred and fifty fossilized mammalian
jaws and five thousand mammalian teeth ("I'm pushing
back into the Cretaceous and doing less and less work in
the Tertiary"); Dr. Jerome G. Rozen, Jr., the Museum's

hymenopterist, whose field research on bee larvae in Switzerland in 1964 led to an interesting reclassification of an Old World bee genus called *Melitturga* ("Up to that time, it had been regarded as an intermediate genus between the subfamilies Panurginae and Oxaeinae, but study of its larvae show clearly that it is *not* related to the Oxaeinae. So, in all likelihood, we can remove the Oxaeinae from the family Andrenidae"); Dr. Richard G. Van Gelder, who became the Museum's Mammalogy chief at thirty and is well along in the second decade of a study of the skunks of the world, with an eight-year published revision of the reclassification of the spotted skunk (taxonomically neglected for half a century) under his belt; Mr. Hobart M. Van Deusen, the marsupial-concentrating veteran of three Archbold Expeditions to New Guinea; Dr. Stanley A. Freed, Assistant Curator of North American Ethnology, who has a weak spot for Mohave Indians ("They build suburban ranch-type houses that wouldn't be out of place in Scarsdale"); Dr. Frederick H. Rindge, Lepidoptera, who has built up one of the biggest and best collections of North American butterflies and macromoths in the world ("I incline more to heterocerology than to rhopalocerology"); Dr. Edwin H. Colbert ("It's only with meaningful collections that you can make meaningful exhibits"); Dr. Wesley E. Lanyon, resident director of the Museum's Kalbfleisch Field Research Station in Huntington, Long Island, where he has finally succeeded in rearing a hybrid from a cross of a captive female Eastern meadowlark and a captive male Western meadowlark ("Hybrids of this sort are very rare"); Miss Farida A. Wiley, now, in her indomitable eighties, Honorary Asso-

ciate in Natural Science Education, who for more than
half her life has been briskly conducting Museum nature
walks, emphasizing birds, in Central Park and outlying
territories ("I think you have scaup over there"); not to
mention Mrs. Carin Burrows, wife of Abe Burrows, the
playwright and comic actor, an Anthropology volunteer
who is working on the ethnology of the Naga Tribes of
Assam—and come, without further ado, to Dr. Junius B.
Bird, a man who has captured my fancy as firmly as Mr.
Gratacap once did.

Dr. Bird, elegantly mustached and quiet-spoken, the
Curator of South American Archeology, was for many
years Mr. Charles M. Bogert's runner-up as a non-doctor
in the Museum's higher curatorial reaches. Indeed, he went
Bogert one better, since no baccalaureate clouded the mod-
esty of his academic record. (He lost his runner-up title,
or non-title, in 1958, when Wesleyan gave him an honorary degree.) His formal education wound up with his
freshman year at Columbia, from which he departed in
1927, thanks to the late George Palmer Putnam, the publisher, a man who managed to attend both Harvard and the
University of California without getting a degree. "I was
living with my family in Rye, commuting to Columbia by
train," the latter-day doctor recently advised a visitor in
the course of a marathon chat in his high-ceilinged, arti-
fact-cluttered fifth-floor office. "One day I sat next to Mr.
Putnam, who invited me to go on a Labrador expedition
he was conducting later in the year. I said I had to work
to make money to stay at college, but the next day I cut
a class to go down to his office and tell him that I had
changed my mind. We made a survey of the west coast

of Baffin Land—now Baffin Island—for the Museum of the American Indian. Bob Bartlett—Captain Robert A. Bartlett, the Arctic explorer—was in the party, and in 1928 I went along with him to Alaska, and later to Greenland, on a joint American Museum-New York Botanical Garden-Smithsonian Institution trip. My interest was in archeology, but we were so busy cruising that we had no time for excavations. We did get some walruses for the Museum, however, and I got to know Dr. Clark Wissler."

In 1931, Dr. Wissler (then head of Anthropology) pointed Bird toward South American archeology by sending him, unsalaried but with travel-expense money, to dig up artifacts in Yucatan and Honduras. "I then suggested to him that with respect to South America the Museum ought to know how long people had been in the Strait of Magellan area," Dr. Bird said. "We were in the depths of the Depression, but there was a little spite money available. Frederick G. Voss, an insurance man, had just left the Museum his estate of six hundred thousand dollars for field work in anthropology and archeology. He wasn't even an annual member. He had come in here, unannounced, with some questions about Indians, and Dr. Wissler, who was working on his great book about American Indians, had seen him, without knowing that he *had* six hundred thousand dollars, and been polite to him. I call his bequest 'spite money' because he had a common-law wife whom he wanted to spite. As a matter of fact, she came in here and raised such hell with George Sherwood, then director—she threatened him with a cane—that the Museum turned over half the income to her and only got the whole business after her death. I can't imagine what she did with her money. She lived in a cold-water flat on the East Side, where she raided garbage pails."

Dr. Bird smiled, and continued, "I told Dr. Wissler that for seven hundred and fifty dollars I could find out a lot about the Strait of Magellan area, anthropologically speaking. I spent the winter of 1932 there, on an island in Beagle Channel, named after Darwin's ship *Beagle*, which had gone there in the 1830s. It was evident—from artifacts of mussel-shell knives, harpoon points, and other fishing equipment—that the region had long been occupied by people who used canoes. I came back to New York with a canvas duffle bag of bones and stones and five cents in my pocket. A couple of years later, with my wife, Peggy—we'd just been married; she works as a volunteer here now—I returned to southern Chile. We spent two and a half years there. We covered a thousand miles, partly by boat—a nineteen-foot cutter we named the *Hesperus*—and partly in a twenty-year-old Model T Ford that I bought in Punta Arenas for twenty-seven dollars. We drove it for a year and a half. We made a survey along the north shore of the strait, way up in the Argentine to Comodoro Rivadavia, and inland up over the Andes to the Pacific side. On our boat, which contained basic provisions for six months, we ate a lot of cormorants and sea gulls. Peggy cooked them. She'd never cooked *anything* before. Sea gulls are delicious if you skin them out while they're warm; otherwise, they taste fishy. We did the whole trip for sixty-five dollars a month, including passage. Stay out of hotels!"

Dr. Bird, who began to get a salary (as well as ex-

penses) from the Museum in 1937, handed his visitor a
few of his Strait of Magellan reports, which ran in part:

> At the present, probably 160 to 200 Alacaluf [canoe Indians
> of the southern Chile archipelago] survive. . . . Small family
> units wander from place to place, never stopping long enough
> to exhaust completely the local shellfish supply. . . . Families
> come together only on rare occasions: for example, when
> they discover a whale that is dead or is in landlocked waters
> where it can be killed; when they hunt the sea lions that
> are whelping at rookeries on some of the off-lying islands;
> or when a vessel is wrecked, an event which is sure to draw
> together all persons in the immediate vicinity. . . .
>
> The equipment necessary to maintain life . . . is held to a
> minimum. A boat or canoe is an absolute essential. The aver-
> age family carries fire rather than matches or other means of
> making it, poles for dislodging shellfish from rocks, a sea
> urchin and mussel spear, shellfish baskets, a harpoon and line,
> a bark bucket or tin pail. . . . All transportation is by water.
> . . . For communication, smoke signaling is commonly
> used. . . .
>
> The newborn baby is washed with sea water. . . . In-
> fants . . . are not well attended. If, when learning to crawl,
> they fall into the fireplace, adults show them no sympathy.
> All children bear small scars left by such burns. . . . When
> the baby soils itself, the mother scrapes it with a mussel
> shell. . . . Children, barely able to walk, were seen seeking
> mussels on the rocks immediately in front of the hut. With
> one or two clutched in their hands, they crawl back into the
> hut to roast and eat them. By the age of four, children
> cook nearly all the shellfish they consume, and begin to
> handle the shellfish spears. They spend hours in a canoe tied
> to the shore, hooking up sea urchins and mussels. . . . There
> are no rules for camp sanitation. . . . Most persons can count
> to five, five being synonymous with "many". . . .

Dr. and Mrs. Bird have three sons, now grown up,
whom they took, as babies, on expeditions to North Chile

and Peru. "It's easier to raise a baby in a tent than home," said the curator, who lives in Spuyten Duyvil. "I'd rather spend the winter in a tent on the Strait of Magellan than in Westchester, where I was brought up. The latitude of southern Chile is similar to that of North Scotland."

Dr. Bird's caller had heard that he was famous for his practical jokes, and he asked him about this. "Well, there's the Fake Brick Practical Joke," he said. "Abe Lincoln is to blame for that. He had a secretary named John Hay, who had a son Clarence Hay, who has been connected with this Museum for more than forty years as a trustee, honorary trustee, and Research Associate in Anthropology. He's over eighty now, and he still has the use of a room here, where, incidentally, he keeps Lincoln's original life mask. We get it out of its box every Lincoln's Birthday and show it to the public."

Dr. Bird fingered a faded, but still patterned, textile on a big table in front of him. "A sixteenth-century Peruvian's pants; I sifted them from a refuse deposit," he said, and went on, "About fifteen years ago, Gordon Ekholm, our Curator of Mexican Archeology, set up an exhibit in the Seventy-seventh Street foyer showing parallels between Southeast Asian and Greater Indian artifacts and those of the New World. He has a theory, not generally held, that trans-Pacific contacts in pre-Columbian times led to an Asiatic influence on Mexican sculpture. He'd dug up a lot of bricks in Mexico that had been used as borders for big relief panels. Some of the bricks were fired with lotus motifs—figures holding a lotus plant —which he felt had been derived from somewhat similar bricks found in Ceylon, Bali, and India. He also thought that some of them *might* have been derived from Chinese frescoes, although he was inclined to doubt this. While he was assembling these bricks and other elements of Mayan structures for his show, he got a pathetic letter from a Chinese student at the University of Chicago. This said that the writer's father had entrusted him with something dug up in the family garden and had enjoined him never to part with it unless he was in desperate financial straits. He now *was* in such straits, he wrote, and was sending his heirloom along. A few days later, into Gordon's office came a package containing an old iron dumbbell. Gordon is a sympathetic man. He was still grieving over the worthlessness of the dumbbell when he received another letter, from a man in Guatemala who said he was sending him an interesting pre-Columbian artifact. In came the mate to the dumbbell. Clarence Hay had set the whole thing up. He had arranged for confederates in Chicago and Guatemala to write the letters and mail the dumbbells."

Dr. Bird smiled, and held up another Peruvian textile. "Fifteenth-century shirt," he said. "It dates from just before the Inca occupation. I found sixty-three of these shirts in one cubic yard of excavation in a house site only an inch beneath the surface. Many of these sites are being destroyed by real-estate developments. I'm trying to have the area where I found these shirts and a great many more primitive textiles—a strip about a mile long—declared a national archeological preserve."

Dr. Bird's visitor congratulated him on the shirts, and he went on, "Dr. Ekholm's bricks, which he dug up in Comalcalco, a Mexican city famous for its fired-brick

structures, were not standardized. They came in different
sizes and were fired with different designs. They were
covered with mortar and lime. As Gordon got them
cleaned, some revealed sketches that looked as though
they had been made by children, some had real artistic
skill. He concluded that they were doodles, made to relieve
the boredom of the brickmakers. A lot of them were lying
around in his office after his show, which was a temporary
one, along with a remainder of numbered, unexamined
bricks that were still coated with lime and so forth. I
decided that maybe Gordon needed another brick to examine. I got hold of a volunteer ceramist in our preparators' department, Robert Sonin, and asked him to make
a brick with a deer head and a Buddha sitting on a
lotus-plant throne, indicating the influence of Southeast
Asia on the New World. I told him to draw some crossed
dumbbells in a corner, to give the joke away. Then I
designed a second brick, with the date 1956 on it—that
was the year of the joke—and a couple of crossed dumbbells mounted on it, and a hole in it at the top, for
hanging. We took the two bricks to my place in Spuyten
Duyvil to fire them. Mine worked out O.K., but the
lotus brick, which was a more complicated ceramic exercise, shattered. Bob Sonin made a second one, which also
shattered. He then made a replica, which he put in his
mother's oven. *It* burst. He now realized that he had
used different clays with different coefficients of heat and
that this had caused the trouble. He made a *fourth* lotus
brick and fired it in an electric kiln at Columbia. We
covered it with lime, and, after marking it with the appropriate number, substituted it for one we swiped from

Gordon's collection. It stayed there for two years, until one of Gordon's assistants, who had been working through the pile, got to it and washed the lime off. He brought it to Gordon, and said, 'Look! This is a lotus throne!' Gordon called me in, and he called in Dr. Walter A. Fairservis, Jr., an Anthropology Research Associate, and they got out all the books. I beat it and hid in the Library downstairs, expecting trouble, but none came.

"I didn't want Gordon to waste any more time," Dr. Bird continued, "so, to give the thing away, I slipped my high-relief dumbbell brick into Gordon's room that evening after he'd left for the day. But he had forgotten about the Clarence Hay dumbbells. He guessed that the 1956 brick was mine, but he didn't get the message. The next morning, in the elevator, he said to me, 'Did you get the idea of those dumbbells from the dumbbells on the lotus brick?' Then he laughed."

"Any more jokes?" Dr. Bird's visitor asked.

"Well," said Dr. Bird, "there's the Grizzly Bear Practical Joke. One summer in the early 1950s, Margaret Mead went off on a quickie trip to Australia to study cultural dynamics and so forth. Her assistants—she has a bunch of girls working for her here—decided to clean up her office while she was away. They found a big tin chest full of junk and put it out in the hall. Bella Weitzner, a staff ethnologist—she came here as a young girl in 1908, and she's *still* here, as a curator emeritus—told me that the chest had some Peruvian textiles in it, so I went through it, and found, among other things, the skin and hind feet of an Alaskan grizzly bear. I suppose they'd been used as a costume for some sort of Indian dance

exhibit, but they had no catalogue number and no identification, and therefore no scientific usefulness, so I put
them in a garbage can. Dr. James A. Ford, our North
American archeologist, came by as I was doing this. 'Keep
them,' he said. 'We'll have some fun next winter.' He
outlined a rough plan. One afternoon a few months later,
when it was snowing, I called him up. I said it was time
to execute the plan. I went to the Library and took out
three books that dealt with bear tracks. I studied the exact
measurements that showed how Alaskan grizzlies walked.
All the bears in the books had four feet, of course, and
we had only two, so, for the front ones, I got a pair
of old mitts and put tin claws on them. Then, to soften
up the hind feet, which were stiff, I dumped a gallon of
glycerine on each one."

At this point in Dr. Bird's narrative, two well-dressed
ladies entered the room. He greeted them by name and
introduced them to his initial caller. After a bit of social
chitchat, one of them handed him two small gold sculptures and asked whether they were authentic. He scru-
tinized them through a microscope, and pronounced them
Costa Rican in style, but copies. "Show them to Gordon
Ekholm," he said, "but don't tell him what I said." The
ladies thanked him and disappeared. "I hope you don't
mind the interruption," he said. "We're continually called
on to identify objects most of which are fakes. These
queries take up a good deal of time—I think the Metropolitan Museum curators are more *protected* than we
are—but some of the people who make them become
donors. One of them used to leave a check—sometimes

for five hundred dollars—after his visits. And remember Mr. Voss. We try to duck dealers.

"Jim Ford had a house in Pleasantville," he resumed, "and so did Gordon Ekholm and Harry Tschopik, Jr., our South American ethnologist. He died in 1956. In line with our grizzly-bear project, Jim and his wife Ethel invited Peggy and me for the weekend, and had the Ekholms and the Tschopiks over for dinner Saturday night. They finally went home. I had brought along the grizzly-bear feet—the real ones and the contrived ones. Jim tried to put the hind feet on, but they were too big. 'You do it,' he said. So I got them on, over my stocking feet. Jim and Ethel then taped the mitts on my hands. There were several inches of snow outside. He drove me, in a jeep, along a nearby road that skirted the Rockefeller place in Pocantico Hills, and I got out and *made* a few bear tracks into the woods. Our plan then called for an approach to the Ekholm place, where I was supposed to upset a garbage pail and make a lot of tracks. But the Ekholms had some dogs who started a terrible barking and scared me off. I edged around the back of the house and got lost in the woods. Finally I got back on the road, where the jeep picked me up. I was feeling rather messy—my hind paws had been smeared with bacon grease, to make dogs follow the tracks—and I said I'd had it, but Jim drove me to Harry Tschopik's place, so I made some tracks there and scratched a few trees with my front paws. I had planned to scratch my initials on a boulder, but I never got around to this. The next day, Sunday, Gordon called me up and said, 'A bear went through my place last night. I heard the dogs barking

and saw its tracks.' Some children in the neighborhood
found the tracks that day. A local Eagle Scout was alerted,
and the *Times* ran a story about a grizzly bear on the
Rockefeller place. I called up the Rockefeller warden and
told him not to pay any attention to anything he read
about a bear. I'm not sure that Jim Ford was satisfied
with me as an Alaskan grizzly. He later left the Museum
for the University of Alaska.

"We don't do this sort of thing every day," Dr. Bird
said, a trifle unnecessarily, and, after thanking him, his
guest went down the hall and called on Dr. Ekholm, who
showed him the lotus-throne brick. "It's very well done,"
Dr. Ekholm said. "A typically Asiatic type drawing with
a person sitting on a lotus plant. Many of the design
motifs in the late Mayan period—600 to 900 A.D.—seem
to indicate a relationship between the early civilizations
of Asia and America. It's a complicated question involving
the assumption of travel which cannot be proved. There
is a consensus of opinion that New World sculpture is
independent of the Old World, but I tend to disagree.
The isolationist trend dominates, and the diffusionist position—mine—is exploratory and tentative, but it is becoming more and more respectable to think and talk about
trans-Pacific contacts. Clifford Evans and Betty J. Meggers,
his wife, both of the Smithsonian, have published studies
indicating that such a contact may have occurred, accidentally, around 3000 B.C., when a Japanese fishing
boat, caught in a typhoon, was swept into ocean currents
that took it on an eight-thousand-mile arc to what is
now the coast of Ecuador, where fragments of pottery

reflecting prehistoric Japanese techniques and designs have been found."

Dr. Ekholm's visitor rose to leave, and the curator said, "Junius Bird is a whiz on pre-Columbian textiles. His analysis of prehistoric weaving techniques in Peru—the oldest known—is the most detailed and intensive ever attempted. Clark Wissler was one of the founders of American anthropology, and the emphasis here has been, and still is, largely on the New World, but there's been a change, heralded by the creation of a curatorship of African Ethnology a few years ago. Its incumbent is Colin M. Turnbull, an authority on the Ik hunting and farming tribe of northern Uganda and the Mbuti Pygmies of the Congo who has recently installed our Hall of Man in Africa. The Museum is noted among anthropologists all over the world as an extremely good place to work. I've given a lecture a week at Columbia for fifteen years, and Dr. Shapiro does the same thing, but there's no pressure of teaching, and exhibition tasks are few and far between. We've just redone the Mexican Hall, but that's the first big display job I've had since 1944, when the hall was opened."

The Bird-Ekholm interlocutor had now developed a serious interest in anthropology, so he looked up Dr. Turnbull, who spends more time in the field than he does in the Museum. "In 1958, I was deep in the Ituri Forest, living with the Mbuti Pygmies," he said, "when I got a letter from Harry Shapiro offering me a job at the Museum and asking me to reply at once. The letter was two months late, so I didn't reply. I next got a letter from him announcing my appointment. I've tried to in-

dicate in the new Hall of Man in Africa how man developed there, how tribal organizations came up, and why
people there have half a dozen wives. Customs that seem
bizarre to us generally have a good, rational, functional
reason; they perform a service to society; comprehension
of them should help us understand some of the enormous
problems of political Africa. I think it's a fun hall. I hope
to go some day to Little Andaman Island, in the Bay of
Bengal, where the surf is so heavy that you can land
there only two months of the year, and where the inhabitants are probably Pygmy relicts. They are allegedly
cannibals, but I don't believe it. *They* deny it, and they
have plenty of food. Even if they *are* cannibals, it would
be an in-group matter. As an outsider, I wouldn't be
worth eating. The Turkana—a herding tribe from Kenya
—raided the Ik while I was around and killed one of
them, but they told me I wasn't worth killing because I
had no cattle. I didn't have any status."

Later on, the buttonholer of Dr. Bird, Dr. Ekholm,
and Dr. Turnbull dropped in at the Department of Herpetology offices. There, in a room populated by a large
snake in a glass box in one corner, he was greeted by a
youngish man in shirt sleeves who proved to be Curator
Richard G. Zweifel. "That's George," he said, indicating
his roommate. "I got her—her name has nothing to do
with her sex—in Mexico in 1950, just before I went to
the University of California to teach and take my doctorate.
She lived free in my office in Berkeley, but when I came
here, in 1954, the Museum suggested that I keep her locked
up."

The Museum's student learned that Dr. Zweifel's specialties, despite the presence of George, were frogs, toads, and *Cnemidophori* (whip-tailed lizards), and that he has brought order out of taxonomic chaos in the classification of such lizards in western Mexico, where he has discovered the existence of an undescribed race in an area hitherto thought to be beyond its range. The visitor pressed on to the office of Dr. Bogert, where he ran into further lizard news. He found the herpetologist, a big man with a suspicious air, gazing intently at a glass-walled box of damp sand on a table in front of him. He opened the box, poked around in the sand, and drew out two pinkish-violet wormlike creatures five or six inches long, which he placed on a sheet of paper. "*Bipes biporus*," he said. "Two-footed amphisbaenids, or worm lizards. Look closely, and you'll see that they have two tiny front feet. The black spots on their heads are vestigial eyes. They live underground, in tunnels, and come to the surface at night. They come from La Paz, in Lower California. They're the first specimens to be brought to New York alive. A friend of mine flew them in in a mayonnaise jar. I'm feeding them mealworms, but they probably won't live long."

Dr. Bogert remarked that he was finishing up an article about amphisbaenids for *Natural History,* a mazagine published by the Museum that has a circulation of nearly two hundred thousand. Asked about his writings in general, he obligingly went to his shelves and returned with a raft of Bogertiana. Its range—from scientific to popular— is indicated by some of its titles: "Isolation Mechanisms in Toads of the *Bufo debilis* Group in Arizona and Western Mexico," "Dentitional Phenomena in Cobras and Other

Elapids with Notes of Adaptive Modifications of Fangs,"
"The Indication of Infraspecific Variation," "How Reptiles
Regulate Their Body Temperature," "The First Voices
of Spring" (to wit, frogs' calls), "The Tuatara: Why
Is It a Lone Survivor?" and "The World's Most Venomous Lizards." On this subject, within the space of a
single essay, Dr. Bogert has jumped from the weighty
to the playful. "The Gila Monster and Its Allies: The
Relationship, Habits, and Behavior of the Lizards of the
Family Helodermatidae," a 238-page Museum *Bulletin*
monograph in which he shares the byline with Rafael
Martin Del Campo, a Mexico City herpetologist, starts
out, under the subtitle, "Classification and Distribution of
the Beaded Lizards":

> Lizards of the family Helodermatidae are unique among the
> Sauria in having grooved teeth and venom glands. They are
> primitive platynotids believed to be somewhat remotely al-
> lied to the lizards of the family Anguidae, from which they
> differ in having (1) no supratemoral arch, (2) the prefrontal
> and postfrontal in contact above the orbit (but not always
> excluding the frontal from the orbital border), (3) the later-
> oventral processes of the paired frontals united on a suture
> below the olfactory lobe of the brain, (4) no parietal foramen,
> and (5) non-imbricating osteoderms, which are present on
> anterior surfaces of the limbs, and on the dorsum and sides
> but absent from the venter, except in the preanal region. (See
> fig. 1.)

It goes on, seventy-nine pages later, under "Factors
Affecting Gravity of Bites Inflicted by Helodermatids,"

> The size, vigor, and health of the victim would be of impor-
> tance in determining his resistance. In general, the recupera-

tive powers of human beings diminish with age. . . . Case histories suggest that more serious symptoms often ensue when the victim is aged or in poor health. Alcoholism may be a contributing factor in some instances, but severe symptoms or deaths following bites can be attributed to the lack of caution exercised by inebriated individuals. Such persons are prone to be more severely bitten and can scarcely be expected to be very efficient in removing the jaws of an infuriated lizard.

When it comes to choosing between a person and a reptile, Dr. Bogert is inclined to favor the latter. He likes to point out that toads are unjustly accused of causing warts, and that in fact they secrete a venom, which, properly treated, may protect man against circulatory ailments by stopping bleeding. He is not uncritical of reptiles, however. "In captivity," he once wrote of California boas, "their feeding is a most clumsy and dubious business. They strike out with numerous misses before they succeed in catching a rat, and then the process of killing by constriction is carried on in a most slovenly manner." There is nothing slovenly about Bogert. A few years ago, on his return from a ninety-day field trip to Honduras with the first extensive collection of Honduran reptiles and significant data on how reptiles maintain constant body temperatures, the Museum issued a mimeographed release which stated: "Equipped with a pistol and thermometers, Mr. Bogert collected and took the temperatures of more than a thousand snakes and lizards."

10

DARE ONE SET DOWN A HISTORY, however selec-
tive, of The American Museum without incorporating an
account of the Great Jewel Robbery of 1964? Are there
any readers so young that they do not recall the exploit
of the three Florida beachboys, one of them known as
Murph the Surf, of whom two (while the third cruised
around Roosevelt Square in a white Cadillac, acting as
lookout) climbed a fire escape to a fifth-floor ledge of
Mr. Cady's Romanesque Revival wing, dropped one flight
to a window of the Morgan Memorial Hall of Minerals
and Gems at half-past eight on a cold, rainy October
night; entered, cut holes in three glass-topped cases, and
made away with the Star of India Sapphire (563.35 carats,
the biggest such stone in the world, the gift of the hall's
memorialee), the Edith Haggin DeLong Star Ruby
(100.32 carats, the "most perfect" ruby in the world),
the Midnight Star Sapphire (another Morgan gift), and
nineteen assorted engraved emeralds, diamond crystals,

rings, brooches, and pins, and other stones, thus gaining for the Museum, without benefit of mimeographed releases, a worldwide newspaper coverage that included four columns on the first page and virtually an entire inside page in *The New York Times?* Not to mention an "as-told-to" article in the magazine *True,* entitled "How We Stole the Star of India," in which the boys revealed that by way of homework for their heist they had cased the joint for a week, during which they had made a nocturnal dry run to the gate of the target hall, where they checked on the watchman's appointed rounds; that on the Night itself they twice crouched (at 9:07 and 9:40) when the watchman, now in real life, so to speak, came around; and that the Star of India burglar alarm, the only one in the room, technically activated when one of them picked up its covering stone, was providentially out of commission with a dead battery.

The team's take, which received from Dr. Oliver the accolade of "priceless because [the gems] were irreplaceable" and was characterized by President White in the 1965 *Annual Report* as "a shocking burglary" (the Department of Mineralogy, keeping its nose to the scientific grindstone, reported the acquisition, in the field, of a notable collection of Australian tektites that year), was followed by the apprehension of the culprits and by a burst of activity in the District Attorney's Office, involving secret negotiations and a ransom payment, that ultimately resulted in the recovery of between eighty-five and ninety per cent of the lifted material in terms of money value, including the two Sapphires and the Ruby. This last head-liner was one of the final objects to be retrieved. Ransomed

for twenty-five thousand dollars, it was picked up, by
prearrangement, in a telephone booth in Florida and flown
back by Dr. Chamberlain, the assistant director whose
previous experience with stars had been largely confined
to his eight-year chairmanship of the Planetarium. On
his trip home, he concealed the DeLong Ruby in a package under his shirt. By way of further protection and mys-
tification, he was accompanied by a private detective, or
decoy, who carried an empty attaché case handcuffed to
one of his wrists. "I'm delighted to have this caper completed," Dr. Chamberlain told the press.

The Museum, which had inadvertently greased the ways
for its off-hours visitors not only by leaving its Morgan
Hall burglar alarm out of whack (the battery's demise
had not been reported to the institution's Protection Division) but by keeping the hall windows open two inches
(for ventilation), came in for a good deal of criticism at the
time. Its security has been radically strengthened since
the caper, thanks to extra private funds for electrical and
radar warning equipment and an increased number of
guards, generously provided by the City, and Uncle
Pierpont's memorial is now considered foolproof. Dr.
Oliver has pointed out that for years he had been beseech-
ing the City Budget Director for more money for more
guards (the Museum had only six after-dark custodians, on
a beat of twenty-three acres), without avail. "I found that
Dr. Parr had called the attention of the trustees to the vul-
nerability of Morgan Hall years before," he says. "The
board took the matter up with the City, but nothing happened."

In any event, the Robbery, although far and away the

most spectacular haul in Museum history, was not a trailblazer. Besides the losses suffered under Mr. Gratacap
in the early 1900s, many items had been removed from
the premises from time to time, among them, in the early
1940s, a dozen Inca-period gold-figure artifacts, taken
in the South American Hall by a man who, chased by a
guard, jumped with them out of a second-story window.
And Dr. Bird likes to recall the case history of a remarkable burglary, or series of burglaries, second only
to the Morgan Hall hoist in importance, that took place
in 1953. "The first thing the thief stole was an indigo
snake," he says. "He was a frequent visitor to the Natural
Science Center for Young People, a sort of small-animal
zoo and natural history exhibit run by our Department
of Education. One morning, he showed a keen interest
in an indigo snake there. This is a colorful reptile that
gets to be about eight feet long. Its fan was a big fellow
about six feet long who looked to be about twenty. 'May
I hold it?' he asked an attendant who was cleaning the
snake's cage. He was allowed to hold it, and he then
asked, 'Would you like to give it to me?' The attendant
said it was at the Museum on loan. The next day, the
snake was gone. Its owner, who was notified, was very
clever. He called the Bronx Zoo—I think he got Jim
Oliver, who was then Curator of Reptiles there—and said,
'If anyone calls up and asks what to feed an indigo snake,
try to get his name and address and telephone number.'
Well, someone did call, and the zoo said it would have
to call him back, and it got his name—Robert Kennedy—
and his address and telephone number. One of our Education people went to the address, in Queens, and was let

in by a middle-aged Mrs. Kennedy. Conversation revealed that she had a son. 'Has he recently acquired an indigo snake?' our man asked. 'Well, I don't know what kind it is,' Mrs. Kennedy said, 'but Bobby brought home a snake a couple of days ago and I wish he'd take it away.' The son appeared, and the Museum man recognized him. He denied taking the snake, but we got it back.

"The Museum took no further action," Dr. Bird goes on. "During the next few months, a big overgrown fellow visited the fifth floor on several occasions, bringing in fossil shark teeth, Indian moccasins, and so on, for the curators to identify. Anyone can come in and ask us to do this sort of thing. One day, he brought in a shrunken Indian head from Ecuador for my opinion. I was struck by the fact that the nits on it were visible, which they ordinarily aren't. I asked him whether he had given it a shampoo, and he said yes. He brought in a good many more Indian things, for expertise, and after a while some of us in Anthropology began to miss specimens, often Indian, from our rooms. He came into my place again, looked at a Peruvian skull, and said, 'I'd like to have one like that.' I asked him why. 'My mom's a nurse,' he said. 'She ought to have a skull.' A few days later, the skull was missing.

"We don't have much contact with Education," Dr. Bird's version continues, "and it wasn't until some time after these losses began to register that we—the fifth-floor curators, that is—found out that our visitor was the indigo-snake thief. I took a snapshot of him, and showed it to a curio dealer on West Forty-seventh Street who sold shrunken heads. 'That's the fellow who stole an Indian head from me,' he said. We decided to lay a trap for him. We put some pieces of Peruvian pottery on a table in Bella Weitzner's office. He came in a week or so later. I asked Bella to vacate her office, and I posted a man to watch it, from a balcony. Kennedy went in with a shopping bag, which he loaded with a dozen pieces of pottery. Someone came in to the adjoining room, and Kennedy unloaded his bag and left. Our security police had told us that we had to nab him with stuff on his person, preferably leaving the building, so we were stymied. We laid the trap again, and Kennedy did the same thing. *This* time, the man on the balcony had leaned out too far, and given his position away. We continued to miss things, but the next time I saw Bobby was several months later—on September 16, 1953, to be exact—when our protection people asked me and Harry Shapiro to come to the Building Service Office. One of the guards had seen a man opening an exhibition case in the Philippine Islands Hall. The Museum police had emptied his pockets and found some coins and a religious medal, but nothing incriminating. I recognized Kennedy. I told the police to search him thoroughly. They loosened his clothes. A key to the exhibition cases and several stolen articles fell to the floor. He was placed under arrest. At the City police station, a composite South Seas fishhook was found in one of his trouser cuffs.

"He denied everything at first," Dr. Bird says, "but it turned out that over a period of nearly a year he had stolen around four hundred items from the Museum, worth about a hundred thousand dollars. He generally unlocked the exhibition cases between nine and ten in the

morning, before the Museum opened to the public, when
the halls were being cleaned and when some of them
were empty. He had taken a lot of valuable material
from New Guinea, New Zealand, and Africa, some rare
carvings from Siberia, and some Navaho jewelry. He had
a great many Indian friends around town with names like
Mrs. Bigmountain Martin and Earl Twobears—a list was
found in his home after his arrest—and he used to attend
Indian powwows at Shinnecock Hills, Lake George, Mon-
treal, and other places. Many of the people he went
around with were Mohawk high-steel workers in Brooklyn. He also had a friend called Mrs. Redwing on West
End Avenue. I sent to see her, in a walk-up, but no one
answered the bell. There was a card on the next door
that read, 'Chief Swifteagle,' so I rang his bell. The chief
let me in and introduced me to a bunch of other Indians.
I asked if they knew Kennedy. 'He gave me this nice
old Seneca flute,' said the chief. 'Bobby knows that I
like to dance, so he gave me this flute.' It was our Seneca
flute. I later got to see Mrs. Redwing. I identified myself,
and she became indignant. 'I'll have nothing to do with
anyone from the Museum of Natural History,' she said.
'I gave them an Indian dress of mine, and it's labeled
as coming from an Omaha girl. I'm not an Omaha girl.
I'm a Winnebago.'"

Dr. Bird promised to have this error rectified, and
Mrs. Redwing was mollified. "She told me that she'd
met Bobby at a Mohawk-dialect service in the Cuyler
Presbyterian Church on Pacific Street in Brooklyn," he
says. "She showed me a Tibetan reliquary that he had
given her. It was our Tibetan reliquary. Well, Jim Ford,

Ekholm, Walter Fairservis, and I made a round of second-hand stores on Third Avenue and in Greenwich Village, looking for Museum stuff. We found plenty. We developed a kind of sixth sense. 'This is a Kennedy shop,' we'd say, and it generally was. In one, we found a Museum Maori feeding funnel with the name of a dealer on it. This led us to a shop in the Village which was crammed with things taken from us. The dealer was Kennedy's fence. We got all of his Kennedy items back, and, altogether, we recovered two thirds of the objects that were stolen. Kennedy pleaded guilty—the evidence was overwhelming—and got two years for grand larceny. He was first locked up in the Tombs—his father wouldn't bail him out—where he was called Chief by the other prisoners."

The runner-up to the Morgan Hall triumvirate had not disposed of *everything* to a fence and to Mrs. Redwing and Chief Swifteagle, however. "Most of the things Bobby took were Indian," Dr. Bird says. "He dismantled one of our war bonnets from the old Plains Indian Hall and gave its eagle feathers away at a Shinnecock powwow. He made similar gifts at other powwows. I suppose you might say that he gave a lot of things back to the Indians."

As far as anyone there knows, Kennedy has not re-visited the Museum. Innocence is the order of the day at the Natural Science Center for Young People. Recently, a very young person who had picked up a pine cone from a box there was told by an attendant that she could have it if she knew its name. "Laura," she said, and hit the jackpot.

11

DARE WE CONCLUDE this account of Morris K. Jesup's innocent attraction—spearheaded as it is today at the board-of-trustees level by such exemplary bankers as Elbridge T. Gerry (Brown Brothers, Harriman), Edwin Thorne (First National City Bank of New York), Peter M. Flanigan (Dillon, Read), Frederick M. Warburg (Kuhn, Loeb), Gardner D. Stout (a Dominick-&-Dominick partner and amateur ornithologist who lately sponsored and helped select the pictures for *The Shorebirds of North America*, by Peter Matthiessen and was just elected president), and Benjamin S. Clark and Alexander M. White (both White, Weld)—with the possible imputation that their institution is a rendezvous for thieves? Perish the thought. Luckily, the diligent lapel-snatcher of Dr. Bird, Dr. Ekholm, and the rest has continued his research and come up with some more useful source material. Dropping in at the big, light drafting rooms of the Department of Exhibition and Graphic Arts, he found its head designer, Mr.

Henry Gardiner, about to go to the Hall of Man in Africa, then under construction. "We've been working on it for fourteen months and expect it to open four or five months from now," Mr. Gardiner said as they gained the scene of operations. "It will have three major dioramas and a hundred case displays of artifacts. At that, we have so many African artifacts that we've had to select brutally. The hall is Colin Turnbull's baby, as you know. What with the current interest in Africa, it's very timely. Dr. Turnbull's approach is in terms of different types of environment. Two disciplines are involved in exhibition— the curator has the concept and tries to develop the story line, and we try to make things visibly meaningful, exciting, and attractive. The African Hall will demonstrate the way people live, think, and organize themselves. I think we've got a pretty good thing going here."

The two men inspected dioramas called Grasslands, The Forest, and The Desert, and Mr. Gardiner said, "The Forest shows Dr. Turnbull's favorite Pygmies—the Mbuti —in various typical occupations. We've tried to give it a cool filtered light such as you'd find in the African forest. The Desert will be bathed in the blue light of a full moon. The Planetarium people have helped us place its stars accurately." He pointed to a large wall and said that it would be covered with masks, most of them given by Gaston de Havenon, a noted collector of African art. Two gigantic ones had already been hung, and Mr. Gardiner said, "I don't want to put them under glass, but the problem is how to keep them out of arm's reach of children. We may hang them higher up with a ledge underneath."

He turned his visitor over to the man who built the dioramas—Mr. George E. Petersen, the Museum's head preparator, who has been there since 1933. "I went to Africa with Dr. Turnbull and collected trees, bark, soil, vines, and other plants for the exhibits," Mr. Petersen said. "Models of the leaves were made in the field from cellulose acetate. Then we make plaster models of them in our laboratory, cast them in wax, and affix tapered wires. There's a lot of handwork in this sort of operation. We have a staff of over thirty artisans. I've been all over the world collecting material for exhibits. I did the Olympic rain-forest scene in the Hall of Forestry. There's some very big stuff there in the way of artificial foliage. Actual trees were used. We're busy right now with the Hall of Ocean Life. The fiberglass porpoises are ready for installation. We generally make molds from real fish, but some are made from old mounted specimens. It's varied work. We're not like a commercial shop, although we do farm out some jobs, such as the Museum's new whale, which is being done by a plastics firm in New Jersey."

The visitor went on to see Gordon R. Reekie, the Exhibition and Graphic Arts Department's chairman, who said that he gave autonomy to his designers and produced a four-page interoffice memorandum headed "The Role of the Designer in the Museum's Exhibition Program," that started out:

A designer may be assigned to a complete exhibition hall project or a section of a hall; he may work on two or three projects simultaneously or design a simple temporary exhibit at the same time that he labors on complex plans for permanent halls. In any event, he is assigned to a project from start to finish and is the liaison between scientist and artisan until the exhibit is completed. . . . The designer is a visual interpreter. That is, he translates into visual form the thoughts and ideas of the scientist. This can range from ingenious display of miscellaneous objects . . . to complex exposition of biological phenomena that have never before been presented in a museum.

Mr. Reekie's visitor next called on a scientist—Norman D. Newell, head of Fossil Invertebrates and a man whose *curriculum vitae* includes a Yale Ph.D., an assistant professorship at the University of Kansas, his undergraduate alma mater (he was brought up in central Kansas, where his father was a fossil-collecting dentist), an advisorship in petroleum geology to the Peruvian government, investigations of ancient limestone reefs in West Texas, and the writing of books with titles like *Late Paleozoic Pelecypods, Geological Reconnaissance of Raroia (Kontiki) Atoll,* and *Permian Reef Complex of the Guadalupe Mountain Region, Texas and New Mexico.*

"When the Second World War broke out, I was a geology professor at the University of Wisconsin," Dr. Newell said. "My students disappeared in droves. I didn't like the idea of being on a university campus without any students. After six or seven months of dickering, I got a green light from the State Department to go to Peru to make geological surveys. Peru provided oil fuels for the war in the Pacific, you know. I spent three and a half years there. We actually found a new oil field, but it was fifteen years before the first well was drilled. The Museum hired me, in my present post, on my return in 1945. This place has changed a great deal since then. It has gone ahead very well, but tax-supported institutions have left us behind. All our research programs required outside financing. We've benefited from Sputnik. The National Science Foundation has been a big boon. Our exhibition program has been somewhat opportunistic. There's a strong tendency for the most popular subjects to get most of the gravy. We have more bird halls than insect halls, for example, although insects play a bigger part than birds in man's history. And we have huge collections of carved jade and cut gems, which are not very useful scientifically, simply because J. P. Morgan and others gave them."

Dr. Newell smiled, and continued, "This is no great marble palace. We don't even have air conditioning. But I'm continually amazed at the good will the public shows for this museum. It's a very popular place. In fact, we are almost smothered by our clientele. We have the same problem Macy's has Christmas week, but we have it all year round. We need some device for speeding the school classes out. We wish they'd let us know ahead just when they're coming. We are gradually getting over our repugnance of the idea that this is a children's museum. I really believe it *is* a children's museum, and that only the children—and perhaps the parents who bring them—appreciate it. They have a great capacity for excitement and interest. They ask questions continually. It is quite astonishing how many of them come here with specimens to identify. We try to make them realize that there are good careers in natural history. We give them literature on the subject. People who come here are much more concerned with learning than those who go to the Met, where they are more concerned with pleasure—I don't suppose you'd call it recreation."

Dr. Newell smiled again, and his caller besought him for a word on his own department.

"It was new when I came here. It was a poor relation," the Fossil Invertebrates chairman said. "It had been a division of Geology and Paleontology, of which George Gaylord Simpson was chairman. Our collections of specimens were distributed through six floors. The fragile ones had been put in the basement during the war. We've brought them all together. I think our field is booming—we plan to open a new Hall of Earth History in the fall of 1968—thanks partly to an awakening of public interest in marine ecology. Many marine experts are paleontologists. Paleoecology is a new idea—learning about the present through the past. Little fossils provide a key to the unraveling of the history of the earth. Fossil invertebrates are challenging. You see the opportunities multiplying like rabbits, but the facilities for research are lagging. It's like wandering around in a candy shop, but you don't have any money."

Leaving Dr. Newell's candy shop, the Museum's investigator made his way to the working quarters of one of the institution's most distinguished lady scientists—Margaret Mead, who since 1926 has occupied a kind of rabbit warren on the sixth floor that includes part of the west Tower looking toward the Hudson. There, a series of cluttered rooms is inhabited by the ethnology curator and a bevy of girl assistants whose salaries are paid out of grants. "I came here when I was twenty-five on my return from Samoa—my first field trip," said Dr. Mead, a brisk, vigorous, emphatic, bright-eyed woman who has since made ten expeditions, most of them to New Guinea

and its Admiralty Islands. "I was taking my Ph.D. at
Columbia, and Dr. Pliny Goddard, who was one of my
professors there and Curator of Ethnology *here*, offered
me a job in the Museum. He wanted me to interpret
ethnology. He thought I could communicate with the
general public. I wrote my *Coming of Age in Samoa*
here. (This book, which is subtitled "A Study of Adoles-
cence and Sex in Primitive Society," has gone through
fourteen paperback printings.) I've written all my books
—sixteen, so far—from this base. They're mostly about
primitive societies. I've just finished one that explains how
American society works. Jeanne! Karen!"

Dr. Mead clapped her hands, and two young women
appeared from the rear reaches of her office suite. Their
employer, who has additionally communicated with the
general public in a score of monographs and *co*-authored
books—as well as in lectures delivered at Yale, Harvard,
Columbia, New York University, the University of California, the Menninger Foundation, seats of learning in
England and Australia, and the Museum itself—instructed
them to collect an assortment of her works for the visitor.
"There is a remarkable degree of continuity here, but the
place has become more of a national institution since I
came," she told him. "The whole outreach of the Museum
has increased enormously. *Natural History*, which it publishes, used to be a pretty sober magazine, but it has
brightened up and enlarged its scope. Museum-sponsored
radio and television programs have gotten us related to
the United States as a whole. I'm designing my new hall,
Peoples of the Pacific, with mechanized dioramas that
can be put on rollers, have their tops taken off, have

color cameras installed on them, and be used to make an exciting movie. In this way, we'll be able to put on TV a replica of something that exists only in the Museum and show it to the world. My lectures here, which are part of our adult-education program and are given in conjunction with Columbia, where I'm an adjunct professor of anthropology, attract up to two thousand people —all our auditorium can hold. I live at the Beresford just across the street north of the Museum, which is like sleeping in the office. You can walk through the subway to the Museum if you put a token in the turnstile. This is great in bad weather, and it will be great in my old age, when I may not want to go outside."

The Museum's all-weather friend, who was sixty-six, was about to retire officially, but she viewed this prospect with equanimity. "The Museum is a magnificent base, and we keep our offices here till we die," she said. "Nobody's papers are disturbed till they die. Look!"

She waved at an accumulation of books, magazines, reports, and papers—some on tables, some on floor-to-ceiling shelves, some in closets—and said, "My problem is space. I have forty thousand stills here, used to illustrate my books and in films I've helped produce. I have detailed notes from eleven field trips. I made two to New Guinea last summer. I have forty years of active files in this office. You can't throw this sort of data away. All our data is good forever. How could I ever move? In general, in this country, we're imperiling the achievements of scholars and scientists after they get to be sixty-five. Universities pitch them out. Many of them are productive until they're eighty-five. I've had many offers from universities and

I've rejected them all. It's boiling hot here in summer and freezing cold in winter, but the ethos is good and you can get everything mended. I've always been very happy here."

Dr. Mead paused to reflect. Then, by way of oldsters in her time who had gone on working productively at the Museum in their sunset years, she cited—besides Libbie Hyman, Nels Nelson, Barnum Brown, Farida Wiley, and Robert Cushman Murphy—Dr. Eugene W. Gudger, an ichthyologist who stayed on until he was eighty-eight, and, after curatorial retirement, wrote "Pugnacity of Swordfish Shown in Attacks on Vessels," "Breeding Habits and Embryology of Frilled Shark," "Fishes that Play Leapfrog," and "Fishes that Swim Tandem-Fashion"; Dr. William King Gregory, one of Professor Osborn's chief literary and research collaborators, whose scientific publications run to three hundred and sixty titles, including *The Monotremes and the Palimpsest Theory*, written after he left the payroll (Dr. Gregory, who was born in 1876, is now in failing health and *really* retired); Dr. Harold E. Anthony, a mammalogist who once discovered an entirely new family of fossil mammals—the Nesophontidae —in Puerto Rico and who didn't clean out his Museum desk until 1967, when, at seventy-seven, he went to California to live; Dr. Horace W. Stunkard, born in 1889, who became a Research Associate in parasitology in 1921 and is still on the campus, studying parasitic worms; and Dr. S. Harmsted Chubb, an equine osteologist responsible for the Museum's great collection of realistically mounted horse and zebra skeletons ("What our Hall of Horses would have meant to your grandfather!" Professor

Osborn once said to Julian Huxley, the grandson of Thomas Huxley), who, emeritus, went right on mounting them until he died at eighty-six. (In 1948, the year before his death, he received a *New Yorker* Talk-of-the-Town reporter and supplied him with information that resulted in an article that ran in part:

> Mr. Chubb comes in from his home, in Palisades Park, New Jersey, to his workshop in the Museum a couple of days a week. There we found him . . . sitting at a table facing one of his latest creations, the mounted skeleton of a donkey immortalized in the act of scratching one of his hind legs with his teeth. "Emphasizes the lateral curve of the spine," said Mr. Chubb, who makes a point of mounting skeletons in action and . . . has spent a considerable amount of time at race tracks. "I got Sysonby, one of James R. Keene's racing stable, for the Museum," he said. "I called on Keene a number of times while Sysonby was alive to bespeak the horse's carcass, but I could never get a yes or no out of him. In 1906, a month after the animal died, I called on him again, but he was still noncommittal. I told him if he waited any longer the skeleton might be damaged. He threw me out of his office. Well, the next day he sent word to come for the horse, who was buried on Long Island. We dug him up, dragged the body to some nearby woods, and did the preliminary dissection and maceration there." Mr. Chubb mounted Sysonby in full racing stride, and Mr. Keene, attending an unveiling reception in the Hall of Paleontology, took a long stare and said, "As far as the action is concerned, it's a perfect picture of my old Sysonby." In the early twenties, Mr. Chubb obtained, macerated, and mounted Lee Axworthy, once the world's champion trotting stallion. More recently, he made an unsuccessful effort to get hold of Man o' War. Mr. Riddle, the owner, buried him in Lexington, Kentucky, and is going to leave him there.
>
> . . . In 1892 Mr. Chubb presented the Museum with some chimney swifts he had caught in his father's Catskills chimney.

"To my dismay," the son said, "I discovered that most of the
Museum's skeletons were improperly mounted—vestigial bones
missing, careless preparation, no thought of the living creature.
I reported this to Henry Fairfield Osborn and showed him a
cat skeleton that I had prepared—this sort of thing was a
hobby of mine. He paid me forty dollars for it and ordered
a raccoon and an opossum at the same figure." In 1898, encouraged by these sales to the Museum, Mr. Chubb resigned
from the machine shop where he was working and became a
free-lance osteologist. "Then," he said, "in 1901, just after
I'd done a four-hundred-dollar horse-and-man group for the
Museum—Intelligence controlling Strength, you know—darned
if Professor Osborn didn't land me on a salary!" Mr. Chubb
proceeded to build up the exhibits that are now in the Hall
of Osteology. He has mounted some twenty cases of lively
skeletons, chiefly horses and zebras. "Every skeleton I ever
mounted is *doing* something," he said. He retired nine years
ago, and the work he has since done at the Museum has been
on his own time.)

"And, of course, there's Frank Chapman," Dr. Mead
continued, referring to the habitat-group trailblazer and
predecessor of Dr. Murphy and Dean Amadon as chairman of Ornithology, whose papers remained undisturbed
after his retirement and who once—in a chapter of his
My Tropical Air Castle called "Does The Turkey Buzzard Follow His Nose?"—sought to solve the question
of whether or not buzzards could smell. "Some of my results leave no room for doubt that the Turkey Buzzard
has a highly developed sense of smell," he wrote. "From
others, exactly the opposite conclusion may be drawn."
"Some do, some don't," Dr. Amadon has said, in a discussion of the matter. "In a way, the buzzard isn't really
a buzzard at all. In England, it's closely allied with the

hawk, and here the turkey buzzard is really a turkey vulture."

"The Museum recognizes manual skills," Dr. Mead went on, in *her* discussion with the institution's investigator. "It takes strength and skill to handle a trayful of specimens, some of them valuable and irreplaceable. The manual people—guards who double as cleaners—used to be the brothers of the cops and firemen. Irish. Now they're Puerto Ricans and Negroes. They have to learn to handle the children. The children have gotten worse. For the most part, our guards are kind and strict. The Museum exists for the children. I've always thought that a museum like ours should be planned for bright twelve-year-old boys.

"All of us here know well the carpenter, the electrician, and the packers," she said, as her visitor rose to leave. "When one of them dies, all the curatorial staff goes to his funeral. We are part of each other's lives. The Museum is an old-fashioned institution, although up-to-date in relation to media. Nobody is here just to make money. I was here fourteen years before my salary went above twenty-five hundred dollars. You can't send your sons to Groton on that. Most of the curators could get better-paying jobs elsewhere, and some of them have, but the ethos is so good that not many are tempted. The Museum gives you great intellectual independence."

The Museum's persevering investigator thanked Dr. Mead and wound up his tour with a chat with Dr. Murphy, the Nestor of Roosevelt Square. "You often hear it said that the curators were more interesting in the old days than they are today," he said. And he went on, from

the vantage point of a man who first received a salary—
for collecting bird skins—from the Museum in the spring
of 1907, when he was nineteen, "Well, Tom Barbour, the
director of the Museum of Comparative Zoology at Harvard, was quite a character. One day he said to President
Lowell, 'We don't have the picturesque characters in the
Yard we used to, do we?' 'Look in the mirror,' said
Lowell.

"You can't compare present men with their predecessors, because contemporary careers aren't completed," the
Lamont Curator Emeritus of Birds continued. "I have
a great admiration for Norman Newell, who works on
movements in the earth's crust. George Simpson and Ernst
Mayr were, and are, memorable men. Once, when he was
curator of the Whitney-Rothschild bird collections here,
and I was head of the Bird Department, Dr. Mayr, who
was born and educated in Germany, asked me if I remembered the boy who had helped me in the Berlin Museum
twenty-five years before. I'd been doing research there
for a week or so, and the director had assigned someone
to bring me trays of specimens and so forth. 'Well, yes,'
I said. 'Nice fellow. What became of him?' 'I was that
boy,' Dr. Mayr said."

Dr. Murphy smiled a senior citizen's smile, and went
on, "Mayr left for Harvard after twenty-two years here
because he felt it offered him a wider field. He's director
of the Museum of Comparative Zoology, as Tom Barbour
was, and Alexander Agassiz Professor of Zoology. He
wrote his *Systematics and the Origin of Species* while
he was here. Dr. Simpson left the Museum—also for
Harvard—after thirty-four years. He was terrifically pro-

ductive. He could write from nine in the morning until six in the evening."

Dr. Murphy, who has written nine books and some five hundred papers on scientific subjects, remarked that the Museum's collections included the world's most complete coverage of the avifauna of the world. "The Bird Department has had three men of great native gifts," he said. "Daniel G. Elliot, who was really its founder; J. A. Allen, who wasn't much of a biologist; and Frank Chapman, who was no biologist at all but a wonderful popularizer. He never understood what mutation meant—he thought it contradicted evolution—but he virtually created the zoogeography of birds. More recently, we've had three topnotch biologists—Mayr, of course; Wesley E. Lanyon, who runs the Kalbfleisch research station; and Dean Amadon. Dean was so wrapped up in his work when he came here in 1937 that he wouldn't speak to people. He's self-effacing, and a good picker of men." (Although self-effacing, Dr. Amadon is resolute in matters of scientific nomenclature, especially when it comes to buzzards. "The large South American hawk called the Gray Eagle-buzzard, or as by W. H. Hudson the Gray Eagle, is usually placed in a monotypic genus *Geranoaetus*, and in most publications will be found listed as *G. melanoleucus*," he has written in a publication called *The Condor*, in a paper called "Comparison of Fossil and Recent Species: Some Difficulties." "Hellmayr and Conover placed this species in the genus *Buteo* . . . and changed the species name to *fuscescens*. This latter change based on the discredited principle of line priority was wholly unnecessary. In my opinion the genus *Geranoaetus* should be retained.")

"How about yourself?" Dr. Murphy's visitor asked him. "My contribution has been in the field of oceanic birds —zonation on the ocean, like Chapman's on land," said Dr. Murphy, whose most famous work is his two-volume *Oceanic Birds of South America* and whose most engaging book is *Logbook for Grace*—an account of a voyage he made on the New Bedford whaling brig *Daisy*, as assistant navigator, to the South Atlantic in 1912–13. *Logbook* was first published in 1947. It went out of print in 1950 and was reissued in 1967 as a *Time-Life* paperback. It bears a legal disclaimer, or claimer, that reads:

> All the characters in this book are real persons, and are called, to the best of the author's belief, by their real names. Any resemblance to fictional or other persons, living or dead, is purely coincidental.

The Grace of its title is a real person—Mrs. Murphy, who gave her twenty-five-year-old husband her blessing to leave her for the ten-months' trip four and a half months after they were married. The book is based on his diary (four hundred thousand words, edited down to eighty thousand), his scientific notes, and letters that he wrote to her. "After reading your letter," one of the last ones concludes, "I no longer have any doubt that the long months we have given up were for the best, and that we can build on them for the rest of our days."

The American Museum has built on them, too. The youthful voyager had been commissioned by Dr. Frederic Lucas, then director of the Museum, to collect for it, and casks of specimens that Murphy brought back helped fill the Central Park West exhibit cases for many years. A sea leopard and some king penguins taken by him more than half a century ago are still on display. His *Daisy*-based observations, expanding and correcting what was known about sea birds at the time—they were not, as had been supposed, aimless migrants—have provided original research for his *Oceanic Birds* and for sixty-seven articles. Their author has led thirteen pelagic expeditions for the Museum since his initial trip. On this, he named a glacier off South Georgia Island for Dr. Lucas, and since then two mountains in the Antarctic have been named Murphy, which sounds confusing.

INDEX

Abbe, Cleveland, 167
Abbott, Clinton G., 104
Academy of Natural Sciences, 17
Acland, Henry Wentworth, 12
Adler Planetarium, 209
African Hall, 137, 138, 140, 143, 144, 155, 156, 159, 160, 209
Agassiz, Louis, naturalist, 11–14, 20, 33, 64, 97, 127, 154, 257; -Bickmore relationship, 13; Museum, 20, 95, 105, 147
Age of Man, Hall of, 151
Ahnighito or Tent, excavated meteorite, 84
Akeley, Carl, taxidermist and explorer, 2, 114, 137–44, 161, 171; African Hall (*see* Akeley Memorial Hall); anti-, 163; camera, 138, 142; Camera Company, 157; cement gun, 138, 142; elephant accident, 139–40; *In Brightest Africa*, 139; medal of award, 141; plan for African Hall, 140; The Wounded Comrade, sculpture, 140, 142

Akeley Memorial Hall of African Mammals, 137, 138, 140, 143, 144, 155, 156, 159, 160, 209
Alexander, James W., 126
Alexander, Stephen, 124
Allen, Joel A., taxidermist and biologist, 68, 73, 80, 94, 95, 96, 98, 99, 100, 103, 104–7, 137, 147, 148, 153, 161, 210, 258; letters from, 63, 64, 70, 71, 99, 103; letters to, 93, 96, 97, 98, 99, 101, 102; *History of North American Pinnipeds*, 95
Amadon, Dean, ornithologist, 255, 258
American Ornithologists' Union, 95, 98, 99, 104; *The Auk*, 96
Andrews, Roy Chapman, 164, 171–87, 203; books by, 172; Third Asiatic Expedition, 175–80, 203
Anglers Club, 25
Annals, Museum publication, 54
Annual Reports, 4, 5, 60, 119, 155, 172, 181, 187; first, 22;

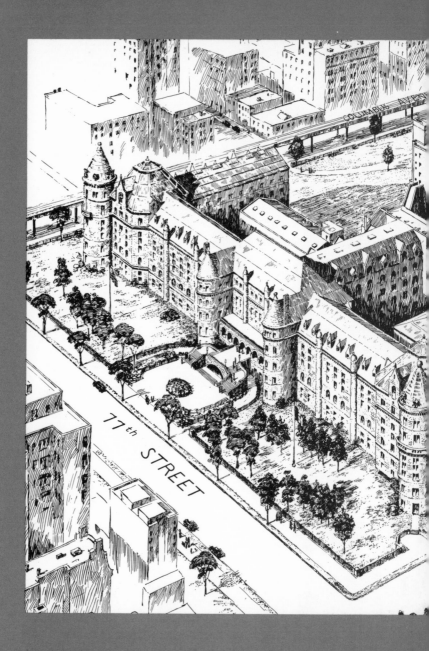